The BEST of The VICTOR

Edited by
Morris Heggie

Foreword by
Andy McNab

PRION

This edition first published in 2010 by Prion
an imprint of the Carlton Publishing Group
20 Mortimer Street
London W1T 3JW

1 3 5 7 9 10 8 6 4 2

Victor ®© DC Thomson & Co. Ltd. 2010
Associated characters, text and artwork © DC Thomson & Co. Ltd. 2010

A catalogue record for this book is available in the British Library.

ISBN 978-1-85375-800-3

Printed and bound in Dubai

CONTENTS

AH, SIMBA, I NEED YOUR HELP. GET SOME OF YOUR FRIENDS AND COME WITH ME!

FOREWORD

The only reason I took a Saturday job delivering milk at the age of nine was so I could buy my *Victor* every week. It was worth getting up at 5.30 in the morning if it meant I could afford to buy my copy – along with a bottle of Coke and a Mars bar – on the way to school the following Monday. It was the perfect read over a slap-up break-time feast, and made me very popular with the other kids.

We lapped up the adventures of guys like Braddock VC, Alf Tupper and Gorgeous Gus; they were the stuff of legend. Of course our heroes were all firm-jawed, supremely honest and played with a straight bat, whilst the bad guys – the 'Jerries' or 'Japoons' as they were somewhat dodgily called – looked scared and dishevelled and ended up taking 'a good bashing'.

These stories didn't always have a happy ending – at least not for me. I remember one particular December edition sparking up big rows at home. It contained an ad I couldn't resist: a very fresh-faced Jimmy Savile telling me that all I wanted for Christmas was the complete new range of Airfix models. If I asked Santa to bring me all the boats, planes and armoured vehicles that Rudolph could carry, I could take a starring role in Operation Airfix. My mum quickly totted up the cost of my impressive list of ordnance and delivered a big 'No' on Santa's behalf.

Our language got pretty non-PC at that point – but it wasn't quite as questionable as the exchanges which punctuated the frequent bouts of fisticuffs in the most action-packed *Victor* clashes. No comic today would get away with dialogue like 'Take that, you great ugly square head!', but when the first edition was published back in January 1961 Britain was still littered with bomb sites, the legacy of the German air raids of the Second World War. And despite its jingoistic tone, *The Victor* always had an unshakeable moral code; it set great store by the values of Loyalty, Bravery, Truthfulness and Respect for Others. By the end of the story, you always knew that the hero had done the Right Thing.

It may take a bit of explaining, but I know what my nephews will be getting this Christmas – and it's not Airfix models.

Andy McNab

Andy McNab

INTRODUCTION

When the idea of putting together this collection was first raised, I was so enthused by the prospect that I never saw a great problem looming. I had been a *Victor* fan as a boy in the early sixties and later as a young sub-editor on *The Rover* comic I read *The Victor* as part of my job. I had enjoyed a great many *Victor* characters who had featured in stories so strongly written that I remembered them all vividly. Herein lay the problem.

With so much terrific material what do you leave out? Painful decisions would have to be made. I re-read dozens of my favourite series and discussed favourites with many *Victor* fans. Was *I Flew with Braddock* and its wonderfully accurate aircraft drawings the best war picture story? Which football tale would readers enjoy most, *Gorgeous Gus* or *The Red Rangers*? Of the many *Tough of the Track* series which one brought out Alf Tupper's true-grit attitude to the full?

So many brilliant series: *Morgyn the Mighty, Sniper Dennison, Wee Bandy, Crib Carson, The Forgotten Fourteenth, The Red MacGregor, Gordon of the Glasgow* – the list of great stories roll out like regimental battle honours. Talking of which, how many of the colourful V.C.-winning cover stories should be included?

I apologise to readers whose personal favourite I have clipped from these pages. My aim was to form the contents into one giant best-remembered edition of *The Victor* comic.

Hopefully, it will give you as much pleasure to read as it gave me to produce.

Morris Heggie

Morris Heggie
Editor, DC Thomson & Co Ltd

BOXING, WAR and MOTOR-RACING in this BIG THRILL picture paper!

THE Victor

EVERY MONDAY

Price 4½d

No. 22
JULY 22nd
1961

THE COURAGE OF SERGEANT JACKSON

One night in April, 1944, Flight Engineer Sergeant Norman Jackson became one of the greatest heroes of Bomber Command when he fought the flames in a blazing Lancaster. The plane had been attacking the important industrial town of Schweinfurt.

LEFT, LEFT. STEADY, STEADY—BOMBS GONE!

FIGHTER ATTACK.

WE'VE BEEN HIT, SKIPPER. WE'RE ON FIRE!

CONTINUED ON BACK PAGE

CONTINUED FROM FRONT PAGE

THE FIRE IS SPREADING. LOOKS LIKE WE'VE HAD IT!

HEY, WHAT ARE YOU DOING, NORMAN?

I'M GOING OUT ON THE WING TO TACKLE THE FIRE. IT'S OUR ONLY CHANCE. OKAY, SKIPPER?

OKAY, NORMAN. GOOD LUCK, LAD.

Sergeant Jackson had a daring scheme to beat the flames.

NOT FAR TO GO, NOW.

BLAST IT. MY BLOOMING 'CHUTE HAS OPENED.

PAY OUT THE RIGGING LINES AS HE CRAWLS ALONG, LADS.

WHEW, THE SLIPSTREAM IS WORSE THAN I THOUGHT. IT NEARLY SWEPT ME OFF THERE.

THE FLAMES ARE ROASTING ME ALIVE. I CAN'T HOLD ON MUCH LONGER.

MY PARACHUTE IS ON FIRE. I'LL BE LUCKY TO GET OUT OF THIS LOT ALIVE!

TREES! I MIGHT BE IN LUCK. THEY MIGHT HELP TO BREAK MY FALL.

The trees broke his fall and he had a miraculous escape. Jackson was taken prisoner, but the tough sergeant got over his wounds. His incredible feat won him the Victoria Cross.

SEE PAGE 22 for the next colour cover story.

PRINTED AND PUBLISHED IN GREAT BRITAIN BY D. C. THOMSON & CO., LTD. AND JOHN LENG & CO., LTD., 12 FETTER LANE, FLEET STREET, LONDON, E.C.4. REGISTERED FOR TRANSMISSION BY CANADIAN MAGAZINE POST. © D. C. THOMSON & CO., LTD., 1961.

The story of the famous book about Britain's greatest pilot of the Second World War!

I FLEW WITH BRADDOCK

SERGEANT MATT BRADDOCK was one of Britain's greatest pilots of the last war. His exploits won him the Victoria Cross and Bar and many other medals. But Braddock was not interested in honours. All he wanted to do was to get on with the war. This is the story in pictures of the famous book written by George Bourne, who flew as Braddock's navigator. It was 1940, when the evacuation of the British Forces from Dunkirk was going on. Bourne had just graduated as a navigator and was at Liverpool Street Railway Station, in London, on his way to the R.A.F. Station, Rampton.

SERGEANT-PILOT MATT BRADDOCK, V.C.

SERGEANT GEORGE BOURNE

Suddenly two service policemen picked on the man in front of Bourne at the ticket office.

THAT SECOND MAN THERE, YOU'RE IMPROPERLY DRESSED! WHERE'S YOUR CAP?

WHERE YOU OUGHT TO BE, OVER IN FRANCE! I'VE JUST COME FROM DUNKIRK. THERE'S FIGHTING GOING ON THERE, MAYBE YOU'VE HEARD.

THAT POOR BLOKE'S HAD IT! THESE S.P.'S WILL HAVE HIM FOR EVERY CRIME IN THE BOOK!

Inside the service police office, the prisoner grabbed the phone.

WHAT ARE YOU PLAYING AT?

HULLO, GET ME THE AIR MINISTRY. I WANT TO SPEAK TO THE COMMANDER-IN-CHIEF, BOMBER COMMAND.

LET HIM CARRY ON. HE'LL NEVER GET THROUGH.

BRADDOCK HERE, SIR. TWO RAF POLICE CLOTS HAVE ARRESTED ME AT LIVERPOOL STREET STATION FOR NOT WEARING A CAP. WOULD YOU LIKE TO SPEAK TO THEM?

IT CAN'T BE TRUE!

THE C-IN-C WOULD LIKE A FEW WORDS WITH YOU.

RELEASE BRADDOCK AT ONCE. SEND ME YOUR NAME AND NUMBER. I'LL HAVE YOU DIGGING TRENCHES AT THE FRONT!

Y-YES, SIR. SORRY, SIR!

HULLO, WHAT'S GOING ON?

" The name is Braddock! It rhymes with haddock!"

'GOLLY, THAT'S THE BOD WHO WAS ARRESTED! HE'S TURNED THE TABLES ON THE COPS!

PLATFORM 3

THERE'S ROOM IN HERE.

THIS'LL DO.

SO LONG, SUCKERS! YOU SHOULD FIND A WAY OF GETTING INTO THE WAR INSTEAD OF ANNOYING THE FIGHTING MEN WHO ARE ALREADY IN IT!

COME IN AND TAKE THE WEIGHT OFF YOUR FEET.

THIS IS A FIRST CLASS COMPARTMENT.

I CAN READ. I SAW IT WAS A FIRST CLASS CARRIAGE.

I SHALL REPORT YOU TO YOUR COMMANDING OFFICER FOR INSOLENCE. WHAT'S YOUR NAME?

BRADDOCK! IT RHYMES WITH HADDOCK!

THAT'S THE FAMOUS SERGEANT BRADDOCK. BETTER LEAVE HIM ALONE.

GLAD TO SEE THE BACK OF THAT LOT. BY THE WAY, WHAT'S YOUR NAME AND WHERE ARE YOU HEADED?

BOURNE, GEORGE BOURNE. I'VE JUST GRADUATED AS NAVIGATOR AND I'M POSTED TO RAMPTON.

I'M GOING THERE, TOO. IT'S NOT A BAD PLACE NOW. I'M LOOKING FOR A NAVIGATOR, AND YOU SEEM A LIKELY CHAP. WE'LL SEE HOW YOU SHAPE, AND MAYBE WE'LL CREW UP TOGETHER.

Later.

In training flights, George Bourne proved he was a first-class navigator, well up to even Braddock's exacting standards. They crewed up to form one of the greatest flying teams of all time.

10

First to fly the Mosquito—the plane that packs a rocket punch!

In all kinds of planes, Braddock and Bourne flew against Germany.

In Blenheims, they blasted bridges in front of the advancing enemy. In Hampdens, they raided German invasion barges.

In Beaufighters, they blasted Nazi bombers from the night skies.

In Mosquitos, they engaged German fighters over the Fatherland itself.

During these exploits, Braddock won the V.C. and Bar and several other medals. Bourne gained his share of "gongs" too.

THIS NEW PLANE OF OURS CERTAINLY HANDLED WELL ON THE FIRST FLIGHTS. ITS ROCKETS WILL PACK A PUNCH.

Braddock and Bourne were the first R.A.F. men to fly a rocket-firing Mosquito.

YOU'RE WANTED AT FLYING CONTROL. THERE'S A BIG FLAP ON AND THEY'RE LOADING THE ROCKETS ON YOUR PLANE.

COME ON, GEORGE.

THERE'S A U-BOAT ABOUT HERE. IT'S BEEN DAMAGED BY A FLYING-BOAT AND IS LIMPING HOME ON THE SURFACE.

THE WEATHER REPORT IS GRIM.

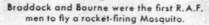

NEVER MIND, IF THAT SUB CAN BE GOT, WE'LL GET IT.

THIS IS THE SORT OF DAY WHEN EVEN THE BIRDS ARE WALKING. I DON'T FANCY OUR CHANCES OF FINDING THE SUB.

I DON'T KNOW, WE SHOULD BE GETTING WARM NOW.

ARM THE ROCKETS, GEORGE. WE'VE FOUND OUR TARGET AND IT'S SHOOTING AT US.

THERE IT IS, GEORGE. LET'S GET AT IT!

" Found U-boat, sunk it! Put the kettle on!"

THAT'S FIXED IT! GOOD SHOOTING, BRAD.

FOUND U-BOAT, SUNK IT! ESTIMATED TIME OF ARRIVAL FIFTEEN THIRTY HOURS. PUT THE KETTLE ON.

After this last mission on Mosquitos, Bourne went off on leave, to be followed by a course at the Advanced Navigation School, while Braddock went to London. He had been summoned to the Air Ministry by the C.-in-C., Bomber Command.

At the Air Ministry.

CHEERIO FOR NOW, GEORGE. I'LL SEE WHAT THEY WANT. IT'LL BE SOME FLYING JOB AND, WHATEVER HAPPENS, I'LL GET YOU FOR MY NAVIGATOR.

ALL THE BEST, BRAD.

WELCOME BACK, BRADDOCK. WE'VE GOT YOU BACK TO THE BOMBERS AT LAST. DO YOU KNOW WHY?

I SUPPOSE IT'S BECAUSE YOU WANT ME TO DO SOME BOMBING, SIR.

RIGHT, BRADDOCK, FIFTY MEN CAN WIN THE WAR AND YOU'RE ONE OF THEM. SIT DOWN. WE'VE A LOT TO TALK ABOUT.

A month later, at the Advanced Navigation School.

WHAT'S THAT NOISE, BOURNE?

IT'S MY FORMER SKIPPER, MATT BRADDOCK, ON HIS MOTOR BIKE, SIR.

THEN GO AND TELL HIM TO REPORT TO THE STATION WARRANT OFFICER FOR INTERRUPTING CLASSES!

YES, SIR!

HURRY UP AND GET YOUR THINGS, GEORGE. I DON'T WANT TO HANG ABOUT HERE.

BUT I CAN'T. MY POSTING HASN'T COME THROUGH YET. I'M TO STAY HERE FOR ANOTHER THREE WEEKS AT LEAST.

HOP ON, GEORGE. I'LL FIX YOUR POSTING. THERE'S A BIG JOB TO DO!

GET BACK TO YOUR CLASS, BOURNE.

WHERE ARE WE GOING, BRAD?

CRAXBY, HEADQUARTERS OF 5 BOMBER GROUP. WE'RE BACK TO THE HEAVY BRIGADE!

CONTINUED ON PAGE 39 — Into action with Braddock and his hand-picked crew!

When goalies wake up screaming, they're dreaming of Gorgeous Gus! He's the dandy of the football field, but his cannonball shooting gives goalies nightmares!

GORGEOUS GUS

REDBURN ROVERS had never had such a disastrous start to the season. They had lost their first four games and failed to score a single goal! Sam Hopkins, the Rovers' manager, was racking his brain one Wednesday morning, trying to pick a team, when he had an unusual visitor.

WHO ARE YOU, AND WHAT ARE YOU DOING HERE? CAN'T YOU SEE I'M BUSY?

MR HOPKINS, I PRESUME. MY CARD, SIR.

LOOK, MR JENKINS, I'M A VERY BUSY MAN. I'VE A TEAM TO PICK FOR SATURDAY, AND—

THAT'S WHAT THE MASTER SENT ME HERE FOR. HE WATCHED THE TEAM ON SATURDAY, AND WISHES TO SEE THESE PEOPLE IN THE SIDE—JOE PRATT OF WESTON IN GOAL, DUNCAN AND POWER OF RANGERS AS BACKS, CRUMP OF WOOLFORD AT CENTRE-HALF, MORGAN OF ABERCROM ON THE RIGHT WING, CARTON OF REDPOOL AT INSIDE RIGHT, AND KELLY OF WESTPORT AT INSIDE LEFT.

AND SO WOULD I LIKE TO SEE THEM IN THE TEAM. THEY ARE ALL INTERNATIONALS! AND NO POSHED-UP FLUNKEY'S GOING TO TAKE THE MICKEY OUT OF ME!

NOW DON'T BE HASTY, MR HOPKINS.

I'M NOT GOING TO BE HASTY, CHUM, I'M GOING TO TAKE MY TIME AND ENJOY THIS.

BEFORE YOU RESORT TO FISTICUFFS, I SUGGEST YOU LOOK OUT OF THE WINDOW. I SEE IT IS TEN O'CLOCK, THE TIME WHEN THE PLAYERS SHOULD BE REPORTING.

SEE!

THERE'S DUNCAN, POWERS, CARTON, KELLY—THEY'RE ALL HERE! WHAT'S GOING ON?

THE MASTER HAS BOUGHT THE CLUB AND ARRANGED THE TRANSFERS. HIS ORDERS ARE THAT MARTIN, DODD AND WEBB WILL KEEP THEIR PLACES IN THE TEAM. THE CENTRE-FORWARD POSITION WILL BE KEPT VACANT MEANTIME.

BUT THESE TRANSFERS ALONE MUST HAVE COST A QUARTER OF A MILLION QUID!

MONEY DOESN'T MATTER TO THE MASTER. ONE MORE THING. HE HAS DECIDED THAT AN ADDITION MUST BE MADE TO THE GRANDSTAND. WORKMEN WILL WORK NIGHT AND DAY TO COMPLETE IT.

THE MASTER?

WHO ON EARTH IS THE MASTER?

The whole of Redburn was amazed at the news of the Rovers' signings.

COO, BERT, WHAT A TEAM! RECKON I'LL BE AT THE MATCH. YOU COMING?

TRY AND STOP ME, MATE!

ROVERS' FANTASTIC BUYING SPREE: STAR STUDDED TEAM TO MEET CITY ON SATURDAY. WHO IS THE MYSTERY MASTER?

Workmen toiled night and day, erecting an addition to the stand, a luxurious one-man dressing-room, fitted with all the latest devices and richly furnished. No expense was spared. This ornate building was promptly nicknamed the Royal Pavilion. Meanwhile, football fever swept Redburn. Then at last came Saturday and the chance to see their star-studded team in action.

The footballer who had his own dressing-room—and a butler!

WON'T BE LONG NOW, BILL.

NO, WHAT A TEAM! WE'LL EAT THE CITY. QUEER WE AIN'T SIGNED A CENTRE YET, THOUGH!

In the dressing-room.

THE MASTER HAS INSTRUCTED ME TO GIVE YOU THIS NEW STRIP.

COR, WHERE ARE MY SUN-GLASSES? IT'S DAZZLING!

YOU'D BETTER GET CHANGED, BROWN. IT'S OBVIOUS THAT THIS LATEST TRANSFER'S FALLEN THROUGH.

NO, THE CENTRE-FORWARD POSITION WILL BE FILLED. THE ROVERS WILL FIELD A FULL TEAM AND YOU'LL TAKE THE FIELD AT THE STATED TIME.

COME ON, LADS. TIME TO GO.

THIS IS THE FIRST TIME TEN MEN HAVE LEFT THIS DRESSING-ROOM FOR THE START OF A MATCH.

GOSH, WHAT A BUNCH OF BOBBY-DAZZLERS! BUT THEY STILL DON'T HAVE A CENTRE-FORWARD.

LOOK, SOMEBODY'S COMING OUT OF THE ROYAL PAVILION!

IT IS TIME NOW, MASTER, ALL IS READY.

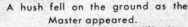

A hush fell on the ground as the Master appeared.

THERE, MASTER. THAT SHOULD KEEP THE GERMS AT BAY.

ALLOW ME, SIR.

GOSH, LOOK AT GORGEOUS GUS! SHIRT AND SHORTS OF SILK—AND HE'S THE NEW CENTRE-FORWARD!

I'LL JUST CHECK THESE CREASES, MASTER.

THE ROVERS' CENTRE-FORWARD WILL BE THE EARL OF BOOTE, G.B.E., D.S.O., M.C.

THE MASTER HIMSELF. HE—HE'S THE NEW CENTRE-FORWARD!

" These people run. It's not gentlemanly!"

I BELIEVE THAT BEFORE A GAME CAN COMMENCE, A COIN MUST BE TOSSED. WITH YOUR PERMISSION, I WILL USE MY LUCKY 5-GUINEA GOLD PIECE!

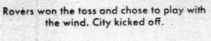

Rovers won the toss and chose to play with the wind. City kicked off.

TAKE SOME INTEREST IN THE GAME AT LEAST, GUS!

LOOK, HE'S MOVING! GORGEOUS GUS IS ACTUALLY ON THE GO!

TUT, TUT. THAT BALL IS MUCH TOO FAR AWAY FOR ME.

Later.

GET A MOVE ON, GUS.

THESE PEOPLE RUN. IT'S NOT GENTLEMANLY!

GET OFF, YOU TAILOR'S DUMMY!

TAKE A GAME, GORGEOUS GUS!

PARDON ME. MY MAN. I BELIEVE I HAVE TO ASK YOUR PERMISSION TO LEAVE THE FIELD.

VERY GOOD.

HE'S HAD ENOUGH HE'S GOING OFF!

GOOD RIDDANCE!

COO! LOOK AT HIM SITTING THERE, BEING FANNED LIKE A RAJAH, AND HE AIN'T EVEN BROKEN SWEAT!

WHAT ARE YOU RUBBING HIS LEGS FOR? HE HASN'T MOVED YET!

The block-busting foot of the Earl of Boote!

Two-goal Gorgeous Gus does his stuff again **ON PAGE 41** —and nearly loses the match for the Rovers!

Seven men against Morgyn—so the strong man sets out to reduce the odds!

SEVEN TRAILS TO MORGYN THE MIGHTY

Morgyn the Mighty, the strongest man in the world, was living in the Ompopo Valley in the heart of Africa. Six world famous hunters had come to the valley with the intention of slaughtering the animals there. Morgyn had driven most of the animals out of the valley, so the hunters and Mowo, their giant Zulu tracker, decided to hunt him instead.

FASTER, YOU BEATERS! I CAN'T WAIT TO GET THAT WILD MAN IN MY SIGHTS.

LET US HOPE HE HAS NOT LEFT THE VALLEY ALONG WITH THE ANIMALS.

But Morgyn had not left the valley!

SO I AM NOW THEIR PREY—AND THE ODDS ARE SEVEN TO ONE AGAINST ME!

I'LL HAVE TO REDUCE THESE ODDS!

But Reventlow was wrong! Morgyn struck noiselessly.—

I MUST BE SILENT. ONE SOUND AND I'M DEAD.

I TELL YOU, REVENTLOW, I DO NOT LIKE THIS SILENCE. IT IS UNNATURAL.

WHY WORRY, BARKER? THERE WILL BE PLENTY NOISE WHEN WE MEET UP WITH THIS IDIOT OF A WILD MAN!

QUICKLY, MOVE—OR YOU WILL DIE!

WHAT ARE YOU GOING TO DO TO ME?

ONE SOUND FROM YOU, MY FRIEND, AND YOU'RE DEAD!

" You should have killed me while you had the chance!"

CONTINUED ON PAGE 45 Morgyn is trapped — in the coils of a giant python!

HE'S BACK TODAY—Alf Tupper, the runner from the back streets who doesn't know when he's beaten!

THE TOUGH OF THE TRACK

"You cheeky guttersnipe!"

20

"Me shoes have been swiped!"

HE'S NOT AN EMPLOYEE HERE. HE HAS NO RIGHT TO USE THIS RUNNING TRACK. I TOLD HIM TO GET OUT AND HE INSULTED ME.

I DON'T SEE THAT ALF WAS DOING ANY HARM. DASH IT, JERRARD, HE'S RUNNING WITH US ON SATURDAY!

I AGREE WITH TARNE. THIS FIELD IS FOR EMPLOYEES OF THE FIRM ONLY. I SHALL ISSUE AN ORDER TO THE WORKS POLICE TO KEEP YOU OUT, TUPPER.

I'M SORRY ABOUT THAT, ALF. DON'T LET IT UPSET YOU FOR SATURDAY. DID YOU KNOW THAT TARNE AND I ARE BOTH RUNNING FOR GREYSHIRE TOO? I'M IN THE HALF MILE AND HE'S IN THE 440 YARDS HURDLES.

YES, I SAW IT IN THE PAPERS. BUT I'M GLAD I DON'T WORK HERE ANY MORE WITH TOFFEE-NOSES LIKE THOSE TWO ALL OVER THE PLACE!

On Saturday the Greyshire team travelled to London by train, under the supervision of Commander Churcher, a famous athletic coach.

AH, IT'S TIME FOR LUNCH. LET'S GO.

I'LL HANG BACK FOR A MINUTE. THEN MAYBE I'LL BE ABLE TO PAY TUPPER BACK!

TUPPER'S SHOES WILL BE IN THIS PARCEL—YES, THERE THEY ARE. IF I WRAP UP AN OLD MAGAZINE IN THEIR PLACE, HE'LL NEVER NOTICE.

Later, in the dressing-room at the White City.

NOW LET ME SEE YOU WIN THE MILE AT THE WHITE CITY, TUPPER!

HEY, ME SHOES HAVE BEEN SWIPED! SOMEONE'S PUT AN OLD MAGAZINE IN ME PARCEL INSTEAD! WHAT AM I GOING TO DO? I CAN'T RUN A MILE IN ME BARE FEET!

WE'LL HAVE TO DO SOMETHING QUICKLY. THE MILE IS DUE IN ABOUT TEN MINUTES. WHAT SIZE OF SHOE DO YOU TAKE?

EIGHT, I THINK.

TARNE TAKES AN EIGHT. JERRARD, LET'S HAVE YOUR SHOES A MOMENT, TILL TUPPER TRIES THEM ON. YOUR HURDLES RACE ISN'T FOR SOME TIME.

WHAT? BUT—OH, VERY WELL, THEN.

YES, THEY FIT ALL RIGHT.

GOOD. BY THE WAY, HAVE YOU ANY IDEAS ON YOUR TACTICS FOR TODAY? YOU'RE UP AGAINST SOME GOOD RUNNERS.

I'LL RUN ME NORMAL RACE, EXCEPT THAT I'LL TRY A SHORT SPRINT IN EACH LAP, TO TRY TO BUILD UP A LEAD BY THE LAST TIME ROUND.

Soon the starter's pistol fired and the mile race began.

"What a finish!"

CONTINUED ON PAGE 50 Alf gate-crashes a private race—to run against an unbeaten American miler!

The Soldier Who Would Not Give Up!

THE Victor

EVERY MONDAY

Price 5d

No. 212
MAR. 13th
1965

STOKES V.C.

On March 1, 1945, during the Second World War, the King's Shropshire Light Infantry were advancing on Kervenheim in Holland. When one platoon came under heavy fire from a German-held farmhouse, Private J. Stokes charged forward.

COR, LOOK AT JIMMY! HE'S GOING TO SORT OUT THOSE JERRIES!

ALL RIGHT, YOU LOT! OUTSIDE! YOU'RE PRISONERS NOW!

LOOK—HE'S TAKEN THEM PRISONER.

CONTINUED ON BACK PAGE

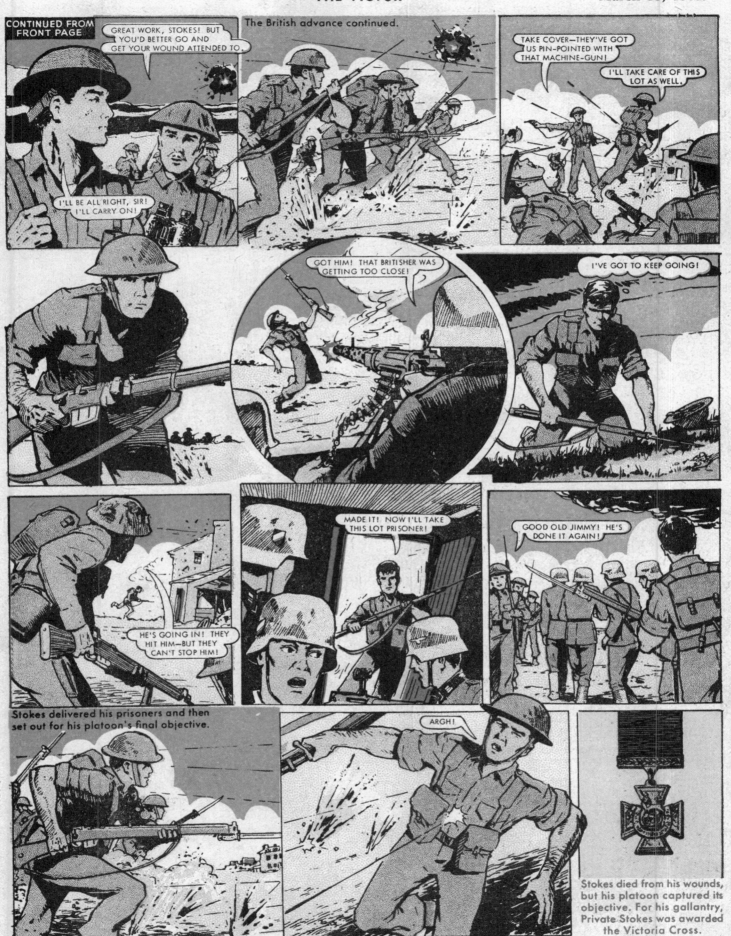

SEE PAGE 34 for next colour cover story.

PRINTED AND PUBLISHED IN GREAT BRITAIN BY D. C. THOMSON & CO., LTD., AND JOHN LENG & CO., LTD., 12 FETTER LANE, FLEET STREET, LONDON, E.C.4.   © D. C. THOMSON & CO., LTD., 1965.

Meet " Moaning Mike " Mahoney—he was always grouching, but he would never let the Pony Express down!

TALES of the PONY EXPRESS

WHAT A NIGHT! I'M SOAKED TO THE SKIN. THERE MUST BE OTHER WAYS OF EARNING A LIVING.

WELL, IF IT AIN'T MOANING MIKE MAHONEY. COME IN, SON, AND TELL US ALL YOUR TROUBLES.

WHAT A COUNTRY! IT DOESN'T RAIN FOR SIX MONTHS—AND THEN WE GET THE LOT AT ONCE. ALL I'M WAITING FOR IS A LETTER FROM MY BROTHER IN NEW YORK ASKING ME TO JOIN HIM, I'LL BE OFF LIKE A SHOT.

AS FAR AS I'M CONCERNED YOU CAN LEAVE THIS COUNTRY TO THE INDIANS. SAY, WAIT TILL I SHOW YOU WHAT I BLEW MY LAST PAY ON.

MORE CITY CLOTHING, I'LL BET. THAT KID SPENDS ALL HIS PAY TURNING HIMSELF INTO A DUDE.

AIN'T SHE A BEAUTY? THIS HAT COMES ALL THE WAY FROM LONDON, ENGLAND. I'LL MAKE THESE NEW YORK CITY SLICKERS SIT UP WHEN I GET THERE.

DID YOU EVER SEE ANYTHING LIKE IT? FANCY GIVING YOUR HORSE A DRINK FROM A THING LIKE THAT!

IT'S PRIMITIVE THE WAY YOU GUYS EXIST IN THIS PONY EXPRESS OUTFIT. ALL DAY IN THE SADDLE, THEN YOU SLEEP IN A DUMP LIKE THIS!

THERE'S AN ART IN MOANING, AND YOUNG MIKE IS RIGHT AT THE TOP OF THE CLASS. I DON'T RECKON HE MEANS IT, THOUGH. HE MOANS ABOUT THE EXPRESS, BUT THERE AIN'T A FINER RIDER IN THIS REGION.

Next day, a change in the weather gave Mike something else to moan about.

WHAT A COUNTRY! ONE DAY YOU'RE DROWNING, NEXT YOU'RE SMOTHERED IN DUST!

IT'S SAFER WALKING! WHY, OH, WHY DID I EVER JOIN THE PONY EXPRESS?

JULESBURG PONY EXPRESS DEPOT

I'M LATE, AND THERE'S SLADE. HE'LL HAVE MY HIDE!

SORRY I'M LATE, MR SLADE, BUT I RAN INTO A DUST STORM, AND—

DON'T GIVE ME ANY EXCUSES, MAHONEY. YOU'RE LATE AND YOU'LL HAVE TO MAKE UP THAT TIME, OR ELSE! NOBODY LOSES TIME ON J.A. SLADE'S SECTION!

ON YOUR WAY! YOU DON'T HAVE TIME FOR COFFEE. YOU OWE US TIME, REMEMBER?

Y-YES, MR SLADE.

WHAT A LIFE. I'M DYING OF THIRST, YET THAT SWAGGERING GUNSLINGER WON'T EVEN LET ME HAVE A CUP OF COFFEE!

The day dream that became a nightmare.

When Moaning Mike was too tired to moan!

CONTINUED ON PAGE 91—The Overland Telegraph stretches out across the West, to rival the Pony Express.

STARTS TODAY:—The story of the Fourteenth Army. They were known as the Forgotten Army, but their bitter battles against the Japs in Burma will always be remembered!

The FORGOTTEN FOURTEENTH

IF THE JAPS CATCH UP WITH US, WE'LL BE WIPED OUT TO A MAN.

DON'T WORRY, OUR REARGUARD WILL HOLD THEM OFF.

EXHAUSTED by bitter fighting against overwhelming odds, the British forces in Burma were retreating before the Japanese invaders. It was February, 1942 and, in the death struggle of World War II, there was no hope of reinforcements for the men of the "forgotten" Fourteenth Army. Their only escape route lay across the railway bridge over the Sittang river.

The rearguard was fighting a grim battle.

LIEUTENANT CHALLIS HAS BEEN HIT.

SERGEANT CLIFFORD!

HE'S HAD IT, SARGE! CLEAN THROUGH THE HEAD.

PULL BACK, ALL OF YOU. I'LL HOLD THEM WHILE YOU GET CLEAR.

TENNU-HEIKA, BANZAI!

I'LL LET THEM GET CLOSE BEFORE I OPEN FIRE.

THE LIEUTENANT IS STILL ALIVE! I MUST GET HIM AWAY.

I COULD NEVER CARRY HIM BACK—BUT I MIGHT MAKE IT DRAGGING A BAMBOO STRETCHER.

I'VE GOT TO HURRY, THE JAPS MUST BE SCARED OF WALKING INTO ANOTHER TRAP. BUT THEY'LL COME AFTER ME SOON.

WON'T BE LONG NOW.

THIS OUGHT TO STOP HIM SLIDING OFF.

The last escape route is closed!

I ONLY HOPE I CAN CATCH UP WITH THE OTHERS BEFORE THE JAPS CATCH UP WITH ME.

Meanwhile, at the Sittang bridge—

RIGHT, LADS, THE ORDER HAS COME THROUGH. AS SOON AS THIS LOT ARE ACROSS BLOW THE BRIDGE.

YES, SIR. THE CHARGES ARE ALL IN POSITION.

THAT'LL STOP THE JAPS GETTING ACROSS.

AYE, BUT IT'S TOUGH LUCK ON ANY OF OUR CHAPS LEFT ON THE OTHER SIDE.

THAT'S TORN IT. THEY'VE BLOWN THE BRIDGE. I'LL HAVE TO KEEP CLEAR OF THE ROAD NOW.

IT'S A GOOD JOB THEY HAVEN'T SPOTTED ME.

THIS IS TOUGH GOING, BUT IF I CAN GET TO THE RIVER DOWN-STREAM FROM THE BRIDGE I MAY BE ABLE TO SLIP ACROSS.

BOATS! THAT'S A BREAK!

JUST MY LUCK! OUR GUYS MUST HAVE SMASHED THE BOATS BEFORE THEY CROSSED THE BRIDGE.

THERE'S NOTHING ELSE FOR IT. I'LL HAVE TO BUILD A RAFT.

THESE CREEPERS MAKE GOOD ROPES.

Sudden death in the jungle!

ALL ABOARD, LIEUTENANT. WE'LL SOON BE HOME AND DRY.

But seconds later, Clifford was in deadly danger.

JAPS! I'LL HAVE TO SHOOT IT OUT!

IF IT'S JUST A SMALL PATROL, I'VE GOT A CHANCE.

LOOK, SAHIB! RAFT COMING.

OPEN FIRE. GIVE THEM SOME SUPPORT.

The deadly Bren gun fire wiped out the Japs.

GIVE ME A HAND WITH THIS OFFICER—HE'S BADLY HIT.

NICE WORK, SERGEANT. GUNNER, FIRE A FEW BURSTS AT THE OTHER BANK. ANY MORE JAPS THERE WILL KEEP THEIR HEADS DOWN.

OKAY, SIR. I'VE GOT HIM.

RIGHT. AT THE DOUBLE, INTO THE SHELTER OF THE JUNGLE.

WE'LL SOON HAVE HIM IN AN AMBULANCE. GUNNER, SPRINT AHEAD AND WARN THEM WE'RE COMING.

WELL, YOU SAVED HIS LIFE, SERGEANT. WITH A BIT OF LUCK, WE'LL ALL BE SAFE IN INDIA BEFORE LONG.

YES, BUT WE'LL BE BACK HERE AGAIN, SIR. THE WHOLE FOURTEENTH ARMY WILL BE BACK—AND WE'LL SHOW THE JAPS THAT THEY CAN'T PUSH US ABOUT!

More war thrills **ON PAGE 79** with the fighting men of the Forgotten Fourteenth!

What's Bruff up to? He's cycling into the American camp with Britain's latest secret weapon!

BOTTLENECK BRUFF *HE ALWAYS DELIVERS!*

IN the bright glare of the afternoon sun, a small boat ran in towards the cliffs near Beachy Head, on the English coast. It was in the summer of 1942, and the coast was mined and protected with barbed wire against a possible invasion by the Germans. However, the men in the little boat seemed to know their way about. They landed safely on the shingle, and stepped ashore confidently.

An officer in battle-dress and wearing the green beret of the Commandos, pointed to the top of the tall cliffs with a cane.

"That's the sort of thing I mean, Clelland," he said to the young naval lieutenant at his side. "See what I'm getting at?"

"Frankly—no!" replied Bob Clelland with a grin. "I should have thought a cliff like that was the last place to try and effect a landing. A man climbing up a sheer cliff face wouldn't stand a chance against the defending forces. He'd be a sitting target unable to fight back."

"They have thousands of miles of beach to defend. They'll concentrate on the flat, open stretches where landings would be easier," replied the Commando.

"Well, that's true enough," admitted Clelland. "The French did the same thing in Canada, when General Wolfe and his men scaled the Heights of Abraham and took them by surprise. And you want to do the same thing in France, eh?"

The Commando officer laughed.

"That all depends on you," he replied. "Show me some gear that will enable me to scale the cliffs quickly and I think we can give the Germans some nasty shocks. "I'm convinced that the best way to invade France is to land in a place where it looks impossible to land, and then fan out along the coast and tackle the main defences from the rear. Quite honestly, I can't see any other way of doing it, because, in my opinion, a frontal assault would be wiped out."

For half an hour the two officers walked up and down the shingle beach, talking and looking up at the frowning cliffs. Ideas were suggested, discussed and either rejected or noted down for further consideration. And then, still talking over their plans, they returned to their boat and sailed away down the coast.

At the seaside town of Sandport, Bob Clelland brought the boat alongside the pier and tied up. He and his companion mounted steps to the decking and after a further chat in the mess, the Commando officer took his leave.

Bob Clelland remained on the pier. It was his base. He was commander of the recently-formed Naval Research and Development Department, which was situated on Sandport Pier. Being an Admiralty establishment, the pier had been given the name "H.M.S. Neversink."

To H.M.S. Neversink came an endless stream of problems.

Now Clelland's latest job was to find some means of lifting Commando troops from the beach and raising them quickly to the top of a high cliff. It had to be 100 per cent efficient, it had to be simple to use, it had to be pretty well impervious to machine-gun fire, shell bursts, and grenade splinters.

"In short," said Clelland, when he put the problem to his team of inventors, "what they want is another blooming miracle. Well, anybody got any ideas for a portable lift, a floating escalator, or a human catapult?"

Professor Crumm, Clelland's chief scientist, was working on a very tough problem already, and hadn't much time to bother about a new problem. In fact, it's doubtful if he even heard what it was all about. Sub-Lieutenant Crow, however, piped up straight away—though it wasn't his job to invent things at all, really.

"But—I say, sir——" he exclaimed. "We are using that very thing right now."

"Oh, are we?" said Clelland. "You do surprise me. Well, what amazing piece of equipment is this thing, Crow? One of those cannons they use at fairs to fire human cannonballs?"

Crow grinned.

"No, sir, it's not quite like that," he replied. "As a matter of fact, I was thinking of that rocket gear they use to shoot a line out to a stranded ship. I mean to say, sir—instead of shooting the rope from a cliff to a boat, why not shoot it from a boat to a cliff? Seems a smashing wheeze to me."

It was a brilliant idea, and like most brilliant ideas it had the essential element of simplicity. Clelland set some of his men to work on it and very soon they had designed a grapnel hook with a powerful rocket attached.

Fired from the beach or from a small boat, the rocket soared to the top of a five hundred foot cliff. The grapnel bit into the turf and the assaulting troops swarmed up the rope to the attack. They improved on their first effort, adding a rope ladder to the grapnels instead of just a rope. And not once did the gear let them down.

Clelland demonstrated it to the Commandos, who were delighted with it, and after that it was put into production and turned out in quite large numbers. The patterns—the three original models—were put into a store-shed on the pier and another job was successfully finished.

WANTED—ONE JEEP

ABLE - SEAMAN "BOTTLE -NECK" BRUFF had a lot to do with developing the grapnel rocket gear. From the small boats he fired the things to the top of the forbidding cliffs. He hauled himself up ropes, skinning his hands and knees, and several times, when calculations went wrong in the early stages of development, he found himself wallowing in icy water.

Bruff was an odd character, and folk seeing him for the first time often wondered what on earth a man like him was doing at the Naval Research and Development Department.

Certainly Bottleneck was no scientist, and although he was handy with tools, being a boot-mender by trade, he was no mechanic, either.

He did all sorts of odd jobs, from helping with simple tasks in the workshops to serving food and washing dishes in the wardroom kitchen. But his main task—and the reason he had been sent to H.M.S. Neversink in the first place—was to " scrounge !"

Yes ! Bottleneck Bruff was the Navy's champion scrounger. It was a sort of gift, like having an ear for music or being able to draw pictures, only Bottleneck reckoned it was far more useful.

He just had the knack of being able to get hold of things that other folk couldn't lay hands on for love nor money, and in a place like the Naval Research and Development Department that knack was invaluable.

Bottleneck was particularly surprised when a few weeks after the grapnel rocket gear had been perfected, Clelland sent for him. Bruff could see that it was something important that was wanted because Clelland was beaming at him.

" Ah, there you are, Bruff," said the lieutenant, indicating a chair. " Please sit down."

Suspiciously, Bottleneck took a seat. A.B.s didn't normally get invitations for a comfy sit-down in the captain's cabin. Something was in the wind. Something big !

Clelland coughed.

" Now, Bruff," he said. " I have a—er—a little problem on my mind just now. I've got to have a jeep——"

" Eh ? Come again, sir," said Bruff. " A what ?"

" A jeep," repeated Clelland.

For once, Bruff was licked. You see this was in 1942 and America had only been in the war a matter of seven or eight months. Many folk—including Bruff—had never even heard of a jeep.

Clelland explained.

" It's an American vehicle," he told Bruff. " A small, open car, very fast and very powerful, indeed. I need an engine for a certain job we shall soon be tackling, and so far as I can see a jeep engine is just about right.

" It's hopeless, of course, trying to get one out of the Admiralty or any of the Service departments—the jeep isn't even

THE TOUGH OF THE TRACK IS COMING BACK!
MORE DETAILS NEXT WEEK

a British vehicle, anyway—but I must have one, Bruff. Just the engine will do, if that makes it any easier, but I simply can't begin to think how you might set about getting one."

" No more can I," said Bottleneck cheerfully. " Not at the moment, anyhow, sir. But don't worry, I'll have a look round and see what can be done. Er—I suppose these jeep things are all the same ? Not different horse powers or anything like that ? I wouldn't want to get hold of the wrong thing."

" No, they're all the same, Bruff," Clelland assured him. " They're small, very low cars with two seats in front and two behind. Their proper name is General Purpose Vehicle, and all American units have several of them.

" Why don't you go and have a look at the Rangers over Munscombe way ? They're sure to have some."

Bruff said he'd do that, and the interview was over. Sighing,

Bruff got out of the comfy chair and went.

THE RIVAL RANGERS

UP to this time, Bottleneck hadn't bothered himself much about Americans. He knew about the Japanese attack on Pearl Harbour, of course, and realised that the Yanks were fighting a stiff battle in the Pacific, but he didn't altogether approve of their butting in on the European and North African fighting.

Certanly it had never occurred to him to have dealings with them. But now, since Lieutenant Clelland needed a jeep

and the Yanks were the folk who owned them, Bottleneck decided that it was time he enlarged his circle of acquaintances to take in the American Allies.

It wasn't difficult. A company of American Rangers was doing training not far from Sandport and every evening large numbers of them came into town.

Bottleneck made it his business to meet them and found them to be cheery, open-handed blokes with plenty of money and no objection to spending it. Although this was all very gratifying, it didn't get him any nearer a jeep.

There were no shortage of jeeps. Bottleneck saw dozens of them, once he knew what they were; but the Yanks had them and the Yanks looked like they intended to keep them, too.

Tentative inquiries revealed that it was every American's ambition to have a jeep and they would have taken it as a personal insult if a Britisher

had been given one.

Bottleneck didn't give up, though. He decided that since he could make no headway with them during their hours of leisure, he might do worse than contact the Americans in their own camp.

It wasn't far to their training area—just a matter of ten miles or so along the coast. H.M.S. Neversink boasted a number of large, heavy service bicycles, so Bottleneck commandeered one and pedalled over to see what was what.

Now, the Rangers were the American counterpart of the British Commando units, and they considered themselves to be tough guys in any man's language. Bottleneck didn't have any opinion one way or the other—not when he rode over to see them. But it so happened that he arrived just in time to witness a practice assault, and after that he was inclined to agree with them !

The assault was carried out by two platoons, one commanded by a lieutenant whose name seemed to be Kolinski and the other by a top-sergeant called " Spike "—a nice, quiet fellow who looked the sort of man Bottleneck wouldn't have minded following himself.

Kolinski, though, was just plain awful, and the way he bawled at Spike made Bottleneck's blood boil.

It was this way. The two platoons came in from the sea in eight assault craft, and after hitting the beach, the troops plastered the top of the cliffs with blank cartridges and then put in their assault.

The idea was to scale the cliff and attack a small stone-built house on the top, and Bottleneck, who avoided strenuous exercise as far as he was able, felt weary simply watching them. It was terrific —especially Lieutenant Kolinski !

The man had a voice like a bull-moose bellowing through a brass tube. He was as big as a mountain and hard as granite. His voice lashed the men of his platoon; if a man fell Kolinski grabbed him by the collar and jerked him up like he was a stick of rhubarb.

When the exercise was over and the Rangers sprawled gasping on the clifftop, Kolinski walked over to Spike and really went to town on him.

" So you finally made it, eh ?" he bawled. " You finally

reached the top ! Call your-selves Rangers ? You're like a lot of old women !''

" Aw, shucks, Lootenant, the fellers is all in,'' objected Spike. " Look at 'em ! They gave me all they had——''

" Like blazes they did,'' snarled Kolinski. " They gave you as little as they thought they would get away with and dodged the rest. You can't handle, men, Sergeant, you're too soft. Why, they actually like you—but if you was any-thing of a sergeant they'd hate you like poison.''

" Look at them men of mine. They hate me, but they'll lick this platoon of yours any time.''

" I've got twenty dollars that says they can't, Lootenant,'' said one of Spike's men.

" So have I,'' shouted another man. " And me—and fifty more —and another twenty,'' chimed in one voice after another.

The top sergeant turned.

" Thanks a lot, fellers,'' he said, " but——''

" Let 'em ride ! Let the dollars ride,'' snapped Kolinski. " You're on, Sergeant, you and them chocolate soldiers of yours. We'll run the same course tomorrow and I'll back my

platoon to beat the daylights out of you. How much dough have you got ?''

Right under the nose of the astonished Bottleneck, they fixed their wager up—a thousand

dollars a side. And then the lieutenant collected his platoon and marched them off on what he called a toughening march.

Bottleneck, who had been listening with growing en-thusiasm, now eased himself

into the nearest group. He nodded—and they nodded back.

" You guys seem to have talked yourselves into one tough contest,'' observed Bottleneck. " Looks like you're all set to

lose a lot of dough, too.''

" So what ?'' demanded the corporal. " We couldn't put up with that palooka's hot air.''

" Okay, okay ! So you had to take him up,'' agreed Bottle-neck, who was doing his best to

get the hang of this Yankee talk, " but it'd be kind of nice if you could win, wouldn't it ? Now, if you fellers was smart you'd have ropes so you could climb that cliff real fast.''

" The idea, feller, is that we train for the real thing,'' said the top sergeant patiently. "This bet is a side-issue. Sure, we'd like to wipe Kolinski's eye for him, but we ain't going to find the Krauts dangling ropes nice and handy for us when we really hit the French coast.''

" Krauts '' was what the American troops called the Germans.

This was Bottleneck's cue, and right away he started in to work on those Rangers.

" Listen, fellers,'' he told them. " I ain't no ordinary sailor. I belong to a place where we really do things, and I'm telling you I can lay hands on a set of gear that'll have you up this cliff like nobody's business.

" It's a rocket-gear with rope-ladders and all, and it makes cliff-scaling as easy as taking candy from a blind baby. Say the word and I'll have it all laid on in time for the competition

and show you how it works, too."

The idea sure did appeal to them, but they eyed Bottleneck suspiciously.

"What's the catch, feller?" demanded the corporal. "Who do we have to murder so you'll give us this gear?"

Bottleneck told them what he wanted.

"It's a deal, sailor," he said, sticking out a big hand for Bottleneck to shake. "You produce this gear of yours and, if it's good and we lick Kolinski's mob, we'll deliver one jeep engine complete."

"It's a deal," Bruff said.

At last, on the day appointed for the Rangers' competition, Bruff loaded up the three sets of gear, pedalled over to the camp, and handed them over to Spike and his men.

"Now, don't forget, you fellers," he said, "it's up to you now. I've produced the gear. I've showed you how to use it and I've let you have a couple of practice runs."

"All we gotta do is lick the hide off that skunk Kolinski," snapped the corporal. "Don't you worry, sailor—we'll do it. Better go grab yourself a circle seat—all the company's aiming to be there, I guess."

One hour later, the eight

assault craft appeared, streaking in from the horizon in a welter of foam. They rammed into the beach, bashing deep into the shingle. Men poured from them, wading waist-deep in the water.

Bottleneck saw the three grapnel rocket outfits carried breast high out of reach of the waves. He saw them planted firmly, saw the fuses ignited—

WRITE TO THE EDITOR, BOYS, LOOK AT ALL THE PRIZES HE'S GOT!

All you have to do is write a letter to the Editor about anything interesting or amusing that has happened to you, or about your hobbies, or any unusual facts that have come to your notice. Each letter printed wins 10/-, and each week two star letters ALSO win one of the special prizes shown above.

Send your entries to:—POST BAG PARADE, "THE VICTOR" 18a HOLLINGSWORTH STREET, LONDON, N.7.

and he kept his fingers crossed.

"Who-o-o-osh! Who-osh! Who-o-o-osh!"

The three grapnels curved through the air trailing smoke, sparks and lashing ropes.

"For crying out loud!" shouted an officer. "What the blazes is going on?"

There was a surging of men back from the cliff edge as the grapnels curved overhead. Then down plunged the six-pronged heads, trailing ropes over the edge as they bounced on the turf.

Bottleneck saw the ropes tighten as men tugged at them from the beach. He saw the grapnels dragged along and burying their barbed prongs into the turf. Then he heard the harsh scramble of iron-shod

boots against the cliff face.

In an incredibly short space of time, the men of Spike's platoon had climbed the rope ladders, and were on the cliff top. They opened fire with blank cartridges, and, long b e f o r e Lieutenant Kolinski appeared, the sergeant had given his orders and taken them in to the final assault.

~~~~~~~~~~~~
FAIR EXCHANGE

THE sergeant's platoon were easy winners of the competition, but it was Bottleneck Bruff who was the hero of the hour. The commanding officer of the Rangers was so impressed by the grapnel rocket gear that he wanted to equip all his platoons with it, and, naturally, he reckoned Bruff was the man to help him do it.

"You're gonna come right back to camp with us," he declared, "and then you and me will work this thing out between us. I just gotta have that gear for my troops—it's the tops."

Bottleneck had the time of his life, nothing was too good for him.

When, at a very late hour, Bruff mounted his bike to return to Sandport, the trailer was piled high with all manner of good things that folk in Britain hadn't been able to buy for years.

Half a mile out of camp, the corporal of Spike's platoon was waiting by the roadside.

"You did us proud, sailor," he said as Bruff came along "—you sure did us real proud. It'll take us maybe a couple of days to—er—obtain a jeep engine for you, but don't worry. We shan't let you down."

And they didn't, either. Two days later, an American ration-truck stopped by at H.M.S. Neversink and unloaded Bruff's jeep engine. And after promising to keep his mouth shut and not ask questions, Bruff had it carried on to the pier and handed it over to Clelland.

"I swapped those grapnel rocket patterns for it, sir," Bruff explained. "I didn't think you'd mind under the circumstances. After all, sir, the Americans are our Allies."

Clelland certainly didn't mind, but he was baffled all the same because the American Rangers could have obtained grapnel rocket gear through the normal channels if they'd wanted to.

He couldn't imagine how Bruff had managed to get a jeep engine out of them in exchange for something they could have got for themselves but he was much too wise to ask questions.

Oddly enough, Clelland got a clue some days later from the local newspaper. According to the newspaper report, a certain Lieutenant Kolinski had parked his jeep outside a Sandport hotel for several hours one night and on returning to it had been unable to start the engine.

The lieutenant was surprised because he prided himself on the care with which his jeep was looked after, but this was nothing to the surprise he got when he lifted the bonnet of the vehicle.

The engine couldn't very well start—because there wasn't any engine left! The men of Spike's platoon had certainly got Bottleneck Bruff his engine all right. They'd pinched it from Lieutenant Kolinski's jeep!

NEXT STORY ON PAGE 94

THE PAPER WITH THE BIG THRILL STORIES TOLD IN EXCITING PICTURES

THE Victor

EVERY MONDAY

Price 4½d.

No. 8
APRIL 15th
1961

Launched in 1939, the German battleship, Bismarck, was then the most powerful warship in the world. The Germans claimed she was unsinkable and she was more than a match for any ship afloat. The British Navy had to keep a big fleet ready to tackle the Bismarck for, if this mighty battleship ever got out into the Atlantic, she would slaughter our convoys. Then, one day in 1941, came the grim news—the Bismarck was loose!

THE HUNT FOR THE BISMARCK

On May 22, 1941, the Bismarck was spotted leaving the shelter of a Norwegian fiord, and the news radioed to London.

THE BISMARCK IS LOOSE! .I'LL HAVE TO TELL THE ADMIRAL RIGHT AWAY!

WE ARE NOW OFF ICELAND, IN THE DENMARK STRAIGHT, HERR ADMIRAL. BUT I THINK THE BRITISH HAVE SPOTTED US. I CAN SEE THEIR SMOKE.

NEVER MIND THE BRITISH, WITH OUR SPEED AND FIRE POWER, WE CAN EASILY DEAL WITH THEM.

CONTINUED ON BACK PAGE

CONTINUED FROM FRONT PAGE

HERE COME THE BATTLESHIPS HOOD AND PRINCE OF WALES.

ACTION STATIONS! WE SHALL BLOW THEM OUT OF THE WATER BEFORE WE ARE WITHIN RANGE OF THEIR GUNS.

TURRETS TO BEAR ON THE HOOD— FIRE!

The Bismarck's broadside scored a direct hit on the Hood's powder magazine and the British ship blew up.

THE HOOD HAS GONE DOWN! WHAT A VICTORY!

In the battle against the Hood and the Prince of Wales, the Bismarck was practically unmarked. An attack by Swordfish from H.M.S. Victorious was rather more successful and the giant German battleship had to reduce speed slightly because of a torpedo hit. The Bismarck eluded her pursuers for a time, but was later spotted by a Catalina of Coastal Command. On the evening of May 26, Swordfish from the Ark Royal attacked.

SHE WON'T ANSWER THE HELM, SIR. THE STEERING CONTROL MUST BE DAMAGED.

With the German giant out of control, the British warships raced in for the kill.

Torpedoes from the cruiser Dorsetshire finally sent the battered hulk of the Bismarck to the bottom of the sea.

SEE PAGE 48 for the next colour cover story.

PRINTED AND PUBLISHED IN GREAT BRITAIN BY D. C. THOMSON & CO., LTD., AND JOHN LENG & CO., LTD., 12 FETTER LANE, FLEET STREET, LONDON, E.C.4. REGISTERED FOR TRANSMISSION BY CANADIAN-MAGAZINE POST. © D. C. THOMSON & CO., LTD., 1961.

All kinds of killer animals escape from London Zoo—but the hedgehog is the most dangerous of them all.

THE MARCH OF THE PRICKLY GIANT

A hedgehog which had eaten specially treated plants at a Botanical Research Station had grown to an enormous size. It had been captured alive and taken to London zoo, but during the night it escaped, wrecking the snake-house and allowing many snakes, crocodiles and other reptiles to escape.

KEEP A SHARP LOOK-OUT FOR THE HEDGEHOG, LADS.

AYE, BUT DON'T FORGET THE SNAKES. THEY'RE MORE DANGEROUS THAN THE HEDGEHOG!

Among the snakes which had escaped was a huge boa-constrictor.

The boa-constrictor could have crushed an ox, but it was no match for the giant hedgehog.

THAT'S ANOTHER ONE ACCOUNTED FOR, THANK GOODNESS!

YES, BUT IT'S THE HEDGEHOG I'M WORRIED ABOUT. WE'VE SEEN NO SIGN OF IT.

IT'S GOT OUT, SIR—OUT OF THE ZOO!

BUSTED A BIG HOLE IN THE FENCE.

SHOW ME!

YES, THAT'S THE WAY IT WENT RIGHT ENOUGH.

WE'LL PUT OUT A WARNING. IT WON'T BE LONG BEFORE SOMEBODY SPOTS THE BRUTE AND TELEPHONES US.

"The hedgehog was a pretty savage hunter."

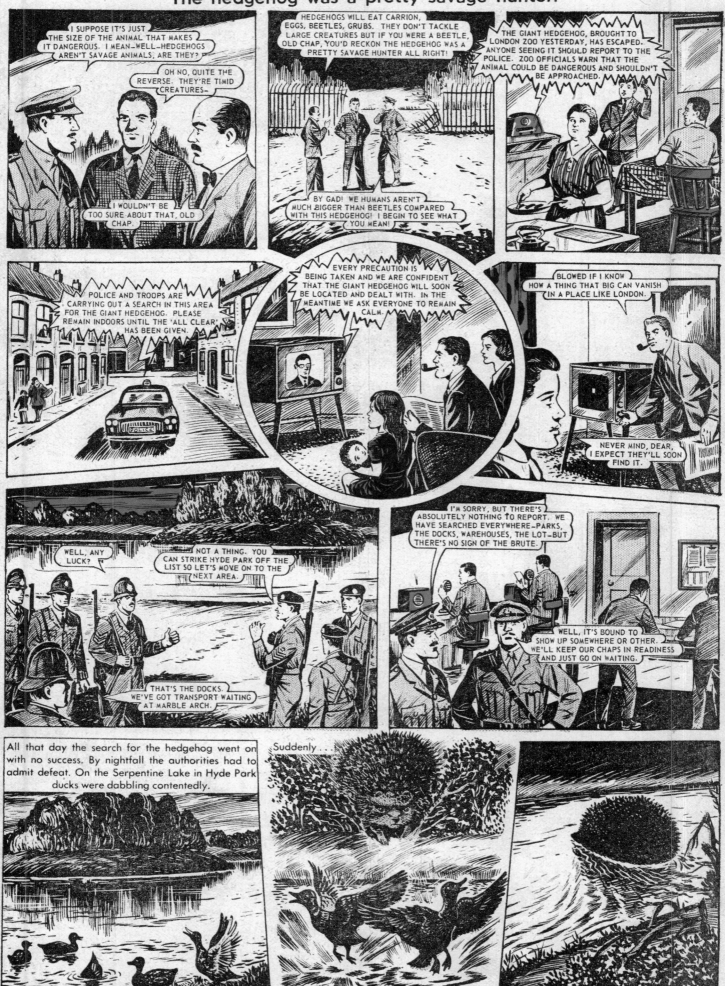

"It seems to soak up bullets like a sponge."

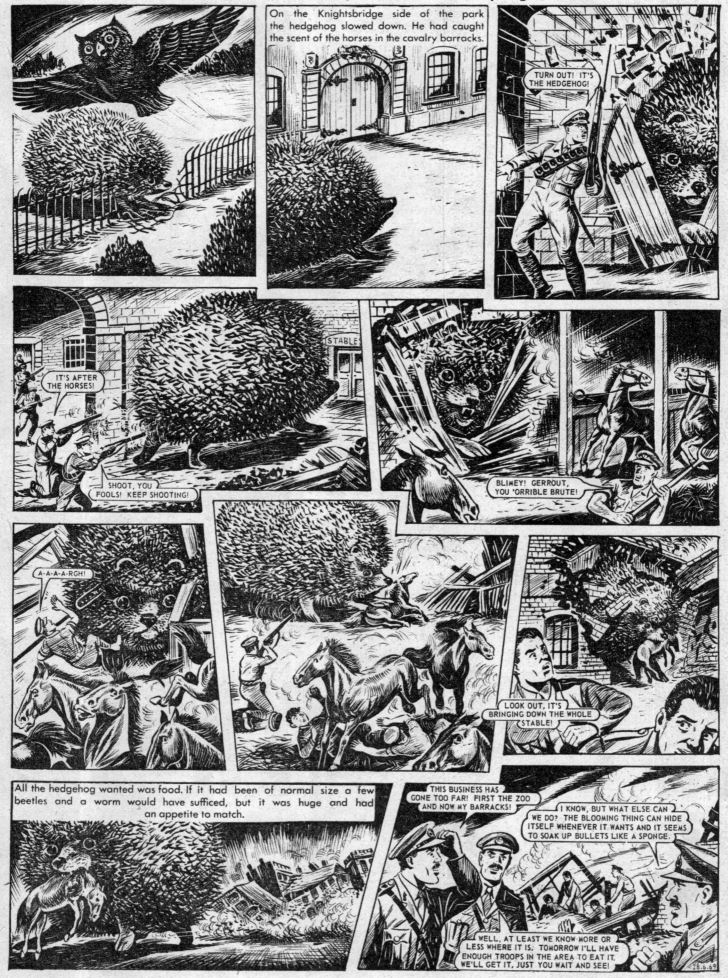

The Pathfinders have pin-pointed Peenemunde — now Braddock goes in for the kill

I FLEW WITH BRADDOCK

Matt Braddock, V.C., was the greatest pilot of the last war. This is the story of the famous book about him, written by George Bourne, his navigator. Posted to Barminster R.A.F. station on a secret mission, Braddock and the crew of his Lancaster bomber, F Fox, found that morale was low and the organisation slack. The commanding officer, Group Captain Mandeville, had a big reputation as a flier, but Braddock discovered he was a phoney. Now F Fox was taking part in a night raid on Peenemunde, in Germany, where the Nazis were manufacturing a secret weapon.

PILOT TO GUNNERS. KEEP YOUR EYES PEELED. THE FIGHTERS WILL BE SWARMING. WHERE ARE WE, GEORGE?

LAUENBURG SHOULD BE COMING UP IN FRONT, AND THEN WE TURN.

TURNING-POINT, NOW. STEER 040 DEGREES TRUE.

THERE'S A GLOW IN THE SKY AHEAD, BRAD. THAT MUST BE THE TARGET. LOOKS LIKE THE BONFIRES HAVE STARTED.

YES, THAT'LL BE PEENEMUNDE.

THEN WE START OUR RUN IN TWO MINUTES.

PILOT TO NAVIGATOR RUDEN ISLAND COMING UP.

MASTER BOMBER CALLING LATECOMERS. SMOKE OBSCURES THE TARGET, BUT BOMB ACCORDING TO PLAN.

IN WE GO THEN, LADS. BOMB DOORS OPEN, TOM.

RIGHT, RIGHT, STEADY. COMING UP NOW . . . BOMBS GONE!

LET'S GET HOME, GEORGE—AND QUICK!

LOOK, THERE GOES ANOTHER LANC DOWN IN FLAMES. THE JERRY FIGHTERS ARE OUT IN FORCE!

YES, WE'VE BEEN LUCKY. I HOPE OUR LUCK HOLDS!

Before it got clear of the target area, F Fox had two brushes with fighters, but Braddock skilfully shook them off and a nerve-wracking journey ended with a dawn landing at Barminster.

" Mandeville's a cheat and a liar!"

LOOK, BRAD. THERE'S MANDEVILLE BACK ALREADY. HE MUST HAVE REALLY SHIFTED COMING BACK. HE WAS SUPPOSED TO BE BOMBING AFTER US!

IT TURNED OUT TO BE A PIECE OF CAKE. SEVERAL FIGHTERS TRIED TO BUZZ US ON THE WAY BACK, BUT IT WAS NOTHING DESPERATE. IN FACT, WE SWATTED ONE OF THEM.

WELL, YOU HEARD WHAT THE C. O. SAID. HOW DID YOU GET ON, BRADDOCK? DID YOU HAVE ANY TROUBLE?

PLENTY, ESPECIALLY COMING AWAY. MAYBE WE WERE JUST UNLUCKY!

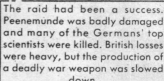

The raid had been a success. Peenemünde was badly damaged and many of the Germans' top scientists were killed. British losses were heavy, but the production of a deadly war weapon was slowed down.

Next morning.

THIS GRUB GETS WORSE AND WORSE. I'M NOT A MAN TO GRUMBLE, BUT—

SERGEANTS BRADDOCK AND BOURNE REPORT TO THE COMMANDING OFFICER'S OFFICE AT ONCE.

HULLO, THIS SOUNDS LIKE TROUBLE!

YOU WANT TO SEE US?

YES, BRADDOCK. THE PHOTOGRAPHS HAVE BEEN DEVELOPED AND I'M SEEKING AN EXPLANATION AS TO WHY YOU DIDN'T PRESS HOME YOUR ATTACK.

When a bomber dropped its bombs, a camera automatically took photographs of the ground below.

WHAT DO YOU MEAN?

LOOK AT YOUR PHOTOGRAPHS. ALL YOU CAN SEE IS COASTLINE. YOU DROPPED YOUR BOMBS AND TURNED SHORT OF THE TARGET!

NO I DIDN'T. YOU DID— AND I CAN PROVE IT!

HAVE YOU GONE OFF YOUR HEAD?

LET'S HEAR WHAT BRADDOCK HAS TO SAY.

LOOK CLOSELY AT THESE PHOTOGRAPHS.

BUT THESE ARE MINE, AND THEY SHOW I DROPPED MY BOMBS IN THE HEART OF THE TARGET.

LOOK, F FOX, I MARKED THE FILMS BEFORE THEY WERE LOADED IN THE CAMERA. I ALSO MARKED YOUR FILMS. IF YOU LOOK AT THE PHOTOS UNDER F FOX, YOU'LL FIND A SMALL A ABLE, YOUR RECOGNITION LETTER, IN THE CORNER.

OH, THESE FILMS MUST HAVE GOT MIXED UP IN THE DARKROOM.

AN UNFORTUNATE MISTAKE, SIR.

I SHALL INSTIGATE AN INVESTIGATION. I'LL FIND OUT HOW THE CONFUSION AROSE.

IT'S A QUEER MISTAKE FOR ANYONE TO MAKE.

MANDEVILLE'S A CHEAT AND A LIAR, GEORGE. I'D HEARD RUMOURS OF PHOTOGRAPHS BEING MIXED UP, AND I MADE SURE IT WASN'T GOING TO HAPPEN TO US.

YOU'LL HAVE TO WATCH OUT. HE'LL BE AFTER YOU NOW. HE'LL DO HIS BEST TO SHOOT YOU DOWN.

DON'T WORRY, GEORGE. I'LL BE READY TO TAKE EVASIVE ACTION!

CONTINUED ON PAGE 64 — Braddock flies on a practice flight more dangerous than most bombing missions!

He looks like a toff, he dresses like a toff—but he's got the toughest shot in football!

GORGEOUS GUS

REDBURN ROVERS FOOTBALL CLUB had been bought by the Earl of Boote, a young nobleman, who had decided to play centre-forward for them. In his first game, he had played at walking pace—but had scored twice with pile-driver shots, one of which had knocked the goalkeeper through the back of the net! The Rovers' supporters had immediately christened their new centre Gorgeous Gus, because of his immaculate appearance. A special dressing-room, the "Royal Pavilion," had been built for him, and he was attended by his butler, Jenkins, and numerous footmen. Sam Hopkins, the Rovers manager, looked in astonishment one morning as he saw the strange contraption Jenkins had brought on to the pitch.

WHAT'S THAT THING DOING HERE?

IT IS HERE BY THE MASTER'S ORDERS. WHEN HE ARRIVES HE WILL EXPLAIN.

THE MASTER WILL BE HERE SOON. TELL THE PLAYERS TO GATHER ROUND. HE WISHES TO HAVE WORDS WITH THEM.

RIGHT, JENKINS. THE MASTER'S THE BOSS!

HERE HE COMES NOW. IT'S GORGEOUS GUS HIMSELF!

GOOD MORNING, MEN. I DID NOT ADDRESS YOU BEFORE THE LAST MATCH, BECAUSE I WANTED YOU FIRST OF ALL TO SEE WHAT I CAN DO. NOW I SHALL EXPLAIN THE FUTURE POLICY OF THE ROVERS.

Gorgeous Gus explained to the players that he had always thought it was possible to win matches without using up too much energy, and this season he meant to prove it. Goals won matches, and he could score goals—if he received the right passes. He was going to show the players how he liked the ball.

THIS IS AN INVENTION OF MY OWN. IT IS CALLED A PASSING MACHINE, AND I WILL SHOW YOU JUST HOW I LIKE MY PASSES. YOU MAY BEGIN, JENKINS!

VERY GOOD, SIR!

THAT'S THE WAY I LIKE MY PASSES. NOW I WILL INDULGE IN SOME SHOOTING PRACTICE.

SORRY, SIR, BUT I'M NOT GOING BETWEEN THE POSTS. I'M NOT GOING TO FACE SHOOTING LIKE YOURS.

THAT'S ALL RIGHT, MY MAN. I HAVE NO WISH TO INJURE MY OWN GOALKEEPER. I HAVE MADE OTHER ARRANGEMENTS!

LOOK, IT'S JUST LIKE THE GOALIES IN THESE "PLAY FOOTBALL" MACHINES AT A FUNFAIR!

Dynamite in his boots!

I'M GLAD I'M NOT FACING THAT LOT. I WOULDN'T BE IN THE BRAMWELL GOALIE'S BOOTS FOR A FORTUNE!

Next day.

LOOK AT THAT. WE HAVEN'T HAD A CROWD LIKE THAT AT A MID-WEEK MATCH FOR YEARS. AND THEY'VE ALL COME TO SEE GORGEOUS GUS!

THERE HE IS—THE ONE AND ONLY GORGEOUS GUS!

When he was ready, Gus kicked off.

HURRY UP THERE. WE'RE ALL READY.

BUT I'M NOT, MY MAN. MY THROAT SPRAY, JENKINS.

COR, WHAT A CARD! GORGEOUS GUS IS THE MASTER ALL RIGHT!

I SHALL PROCEED TO THE OTHER GOAL AREA, WHERE I SHALL AWAIT SOME SHREWD PASSES.

HURRY, NOW, I'M WAITING.

HARK AT HIS LORDSHIP!

THERE NOW, THAT'S JUST THE WAY YOU LIKE 'EM!

GOSH! THEY TOLD ME HE HAD DYNAMITE IN HIS BOOTS AND, BOY, THEY WEREN'T KIDDING!

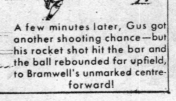

A few minutes later, Gus got another shooting chance—but his rocket shot hit the bar and the ball rebounded far upfield, to Bramwell's unmarked centre-forward!

When the ball boys are OUTSIDE the park.

THANKS, GUS.

TUT, TUT, MOST UNFORTUNATE. I SHALL HAVE TO MAKE AMENDS!

And make amends he did!

Outside the stadium.

THAT'S ANOTHER FOR GUS. I BET WE'RE THE ONLY CLUB THAT HAS BALL BOYS OUTSIDE THE PARK!

Soon afterwards, Gus received a perfect pass.

YOU DIVED THE WRONG WAY!

WELL, WHICH WAY WOULD YOU DIVE? THANK GOODNESS IT'S NEAR HALF-TIME. I CAN BREATHE AGAIN!

THE MASTER'S COMPLIMENTS. HE CONSIDERS HE HAS DONE HIS DUTY FOR THIS PARTICULAR MATCH, AND HIS PRESENCE IS NO LONGER REQUIRED. YOU WILL THEREFORE PLAY THE SECOND HALF WITH TEN MEN!

In the second half, Bramwell attacked strongly.

GOAL!

BRAMWELL'S TOUGH TACTICS ARE BEGINNING TO PAY OFF!

Later, Bramwell equalised.

WE WANT GUS!

WHERE'S GORGEOUS GUS?

GORGEOUS GUS—ER—THE MASTER MUST COME BACK. IT'S THREE ALL AND WE LOOK LIKE LOSING.

I'M SORRY, BUT HE HAS ALREADY LEFT. COME WITH ME, AND I'LL SEE IF I CAN FIND HIM!

THIS WAY, MR HOPKINS. I THINK WE'LL FIND THE MASTER HERE!

PORTLAND CLUB TURKISH BATHS

AH, JENKINS AND MR HOPKINS! WHAT CAN I DO FOR YOU?

THE ROVERS NEED YOU, BRAMWELL HAVE EQUALISED AND LOOK LIKE WINNING!

The match-winner in the gorgeous dressing-gown.

GET ME MY DRESSING GOWN, JENKINS. WE LEAVE AT ONCE.

NO JENKINS, WE'RE IN A HURRY. WE'LL USE MY CAR!

BUT WILL THAT THING GO?

YOU MUSTN'T JUDGE BY APPEARANCES, MR HOPKINS!

WHAT'S THIS THING GOT, AN AEROPLANE ENGINE?

THERE CAN'T BE MUCH TIME LEFT. I MUST HURRY.

PLAYERS ONLY

Gus put on his football boots, and strode out.

BUT YOUR STRIP, MASTER!

NO TIME, JENKINS. I'LL GO AS I AM.

HAVE I YOUR PERMISSION TO RETURN, MY MAN?

RIGHT.

COO, LOOK AT GUS. HEY, YOU'LL CATCH YOUR DEATH OF COLD, MATE!

GOOD, GUS IS BACK. NOW IT'S UP TO ME TO GET THE BALL TO HIM FOR THE WINNER.

I'M GETTING OUT OF HERE, I THOUGHT HE'D GONE!

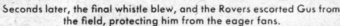

Seconds later, the final whistle blew, and the Rovers escorted Gus from the field, protecting him from the eager fans.

THANKS, MEN. I HAVE A GREAT DISLIKE OF THESE EXCITED DEMONSTRATIONS.

HEY, YOU'RE SURE SWEATING, BOSS.

NO WONDER! IT'S THE FIRST TIME I'VE HAD TO TAKE A TURKISH BATH TO WIN A FOOTBALL MATCH!

CONTINUED ON PAGE 67 —Rovers get a new player and the manager gets the shock of his life!

Morgyn is attacked by a giant python—and if he makes a sound he'll die!

SEVEN TRAILS TO MORGYN THE MIGHTY

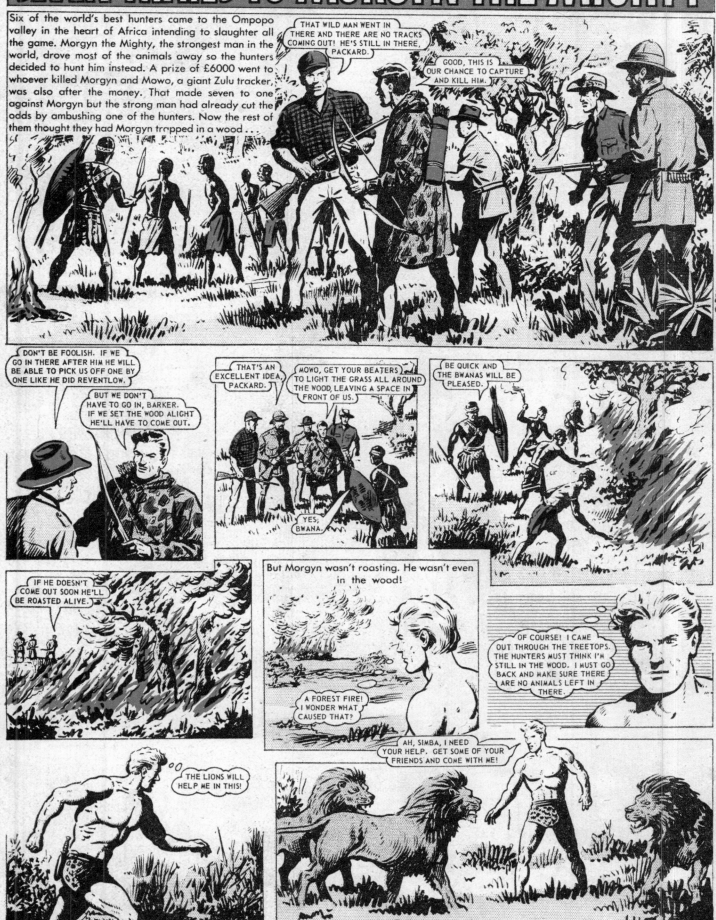

"Do not kill them."

" I'll finish it for good!"

Morgyn was right. Packard was passing close by and the slightest sound of Morgyn's struggle would have been heard.

The grim struggle continued but slowly Morgyn's tremendous strength began to tell . . .

CONTINUED ON PAGE 71 — Morgyn falls into a hunter's trap!

The Picture Story Paper With The **BIG THRILL** Pictures And Stories!

THE Victor

EVERY MONDAY

Price 4½d

No. 41 DEC. 2nd 1961

THE LEGLESS WONDER

One of the most amazing air aces of the last war was Wing Commander Douglas Bader, D.S.O. and Bar, D.F.C. and Bar. A great fighter pilot and tactician, Bader shot down 20 enemy planes—and he had no legs!

In 1931, Bader was one of Britain's leading stunt pilots. Then one day he tried too daring a stunt and crashed.

DOUG'S IN A REAL MESS. I DOUBT HE'S HAD IT!

HOW IS DOUGLAS, DOCTOR?

WE'VE HAD TO AMPUTATE BOTH LEGS, I'M AFRAID. HE'LL NEVER WALK OR FLY AGAIN!

CONTINUED ON BACK PAGE

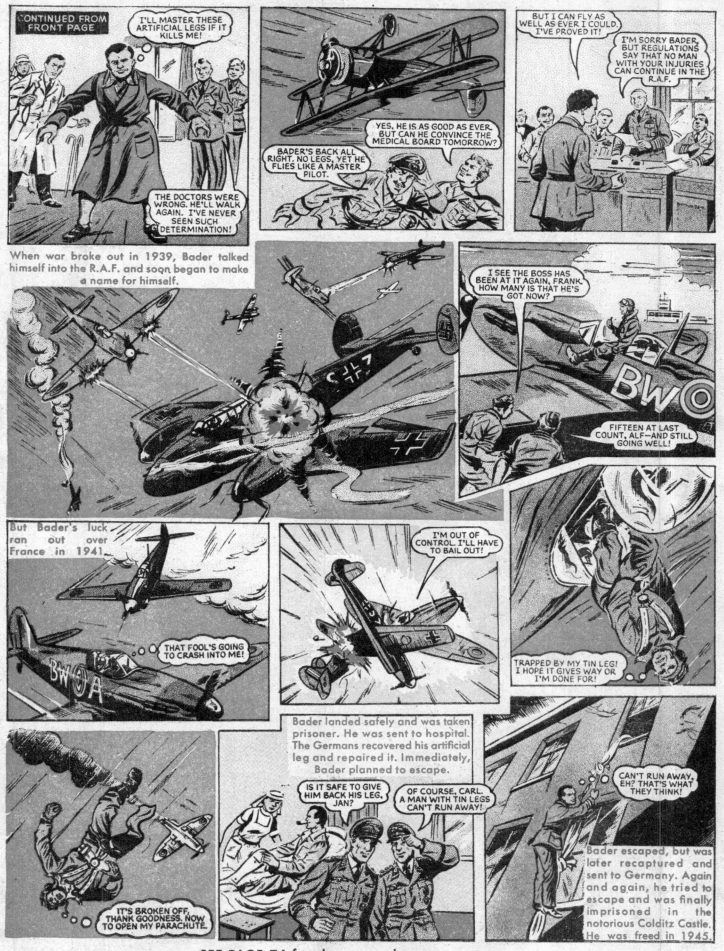

When war broke out in 1939, Bader talked himself into the R.A.F. and soon began to make a name for himself.

But Bader's luck ran out over France in 1941.

Bader landed safely and was taken prisoner. He was sent to hospital. The Germans recovered his artificial leg and repaired it. Immediately, Bader planned to escape.

Bader escaped, but was later recaptured and sent to Germany. Again and again, he tried to escape and was finally imprisoned in the notorious Colditz Castle. He was freed in 1945.

SEE PAGE 74 for the next colour cover story.

PRINTED AND PUBLISHED IN GREAT BRITAIN BY D. C. THOMSON & CO., LTD. AND JOHN LENG & CO., LTD., 12 FETTER LANE, FLEET STREET, LONDON, E.C.4. REGISTERED FOR TRANSMISSION BY CANADIAN MAGAZINE POST. © D. C. THOMSON & CO., LTD., 1961.

The runner from the back streets gate-crashes a private race—determined to defeat an unbeaten American miler!

THE TOUGH OF THE TRACK

" I ain't going to be last!"

"You'd never beat me again!"

CONTINUED ON PAGE 76 Morrow turns up late at Linford — and Alf has to run two mile races!

Cadman shows his true colours when he comes up against the Black Baron—a German fighter ace!

CADMAN THE FLYING COWARD

Cadman becomes a laughing-stock.

" Now you can really even scores with the Black Baron!"

Everyone is talking about Joe Doone, the mystery bowler who had to go to cricket school to learn the rules before he played for England!

IS IT CRICKET?

The first Test Match of the 1961 Australian tour of England had been a disaster for England, but 18-year-old Joe Doone had brought hope to the selectors. Ted Stevens, sports reporter of the Daily Clarion, had discovered Joe in the wilds of the West Country. The Clarion had persuaded the selectors to give Joe his chance in the second Test—although Joe had never played cricket in his life. Now the whole country was talking about the mystery bowler who had hit the headlines.

Clarion

JOE DOONE TO PLAY FOR ENGLAND

MYSTERY BOWLER IMPRESSES SELECTORS IN SECRET TRIAL

NEW DISCOVERY WILL SKITTLE AUSSIE BATS

The headlines caught the eye of Brandon Marsh, a freelance reporter who would do anything for money.

SO THE DAILY CLARION HAVE GOT THE SELECTORS TO PICK THEIR MAN. IF I CAN FIND OUT WHERE HE IS, THERE MIGHT BE SOMETHING IN IT FOR ME.

THE CRICKET COLUMNS OF THE CLARION ARE ALWAYS SIGNED BY TED STEVENS. IF I TAIL HIM PERHAPS HE'LL LEAD ME TO THIS JOE DOONE.

Next day, Marsh waited outside the Clarion office.

THERE GOES STEVENS NOW.

AH! THIS COULD BE WHERE THEY'RE HIDING DOONE.

WESTSHIRE COUNTY CRICKET CLUB

AND YOU THINK WESTSHIRE HAVE A GOOD CHANCE OF WINNING THE CHAMPIONSHIP THIS YEAR, DO YOU, TOM?

BAH! THIS IS JUST A ROUTINE CALL. I KNOW ALL THESE CRICKETERS BY SIGHT, AND NONE OF THEM IS DOONE.

Marsh continued to follow Ted Stevens—with no success.

GOODBYE, TED. JUST LET ME KNOW IF YOU WANT ANY MORE ON LEAGUE CRICKET.

ANOTHER BLANK!

Meanwhile, at Carter's Cricket School outside London, Joe met some of England's top batsmen.

THIS IS JOE DOONE, LADS. HE'S THE MAN WE HOPE WILL SKITTLE THE AUSSIE BATSMEN. I'M ASKING YOU ALL TO LET NO ONE KNOW HE'S HERE, IN CASE THE AUSSIES SEND A SPY.

OKAY, WE PROMISE. NOW LET'S GIVE HIM SOME PRACTICE.

WATCH WHERE YOU PUT YOUR FEET, JOE!

" Your wrong 'un's a winner, Joe!"

LOOK AT THE HEIGHT THE BALL IS GOING! IT MUST HAVE SLIPPED.

GOSH!

SPOT ON, JOE!

All the batsmen tried, but none could combat Joe's high, drooping ball, his wrong 'un.

YOUR WRONG 'UN'S A WINNER, JOE. IT'S IMPOSSIBLE TO STOP IT.

IT WILL CERTAINLY GIVE THE AUSSIES A SHOCK.

Brandon Marsh had just spent another fruitless day following Stevens.

FOLLOWING STEVENS IS GETTING ME NOWHERE. I'LL TRY SOMETHING ELSE. WHAT ABOUT OLD CARTER? HE USED TO WRITE COACHING ARTICLES FOR THE CLARION AND HE'S A PAL OF STEVEN'S. IT'S WORTH A TRY ANYWAY.

CAN I SEE MISTER CARTER? I WANT TO TAKE SOME CRICKET LESSONS.

CARTER'S CRICKET SCHOOL

SORRY! MR CARTER IS TAKING ON NO MORE PUPILS MEANTIME.

THAT'S SUSPICIOUS. I'LL CLIMB UP THE WALL ROUND THE CORNER AND HAVE A LOOK.

CARTER'S SCHOOL

THAT SETTLES IT. I BET THAT MAN IS ANOTHER GUARD TO KEEP SPIES AWAY FROM DOONE WHILE HE PRACTISES.

That evening.

THAT'S STEVENS' HOUSE—WHERE THAT LAD IS WORKING IN THE GARDEN. I MIGHT HAVE MORE LUCK HERE.

THAT CAT WILL CATCH THE BIRD IF I DON'T DO SOMETHING!

A DEAD SHOT! AND WITH A BOWLING ACTION TOO!

Trapped by the smooth talking stranger!

CONTINUED ON PAGE 111 Don't miss the thrills of the hunt for Joe Doone.

Wee Bandy goes to Vienna for the semi-final of the European Cup—but he doesn't play!

WEE BANDY

PRESSLEY RANGERS, the First Division team, had been knocked out of the F.A. Cup, but were challenging for the League Championship and were in the semi-final of the European Cup. One of their stars was Willie Brown, a farmhand nicknamed Wee Bandy. Bandy was a bundle of energy who never stopped running. One day at training—

I'LL STOP THE GAME FOR A MINUTE.

LOOK! WEE BANDY HAS BELTED THE MANAGER, MISTER SIMS!

THE KID WON'T STOP FOR ANYONE.

I'M SORRY, BOSS. I DIDN'T SEE IT WAS YOU.

NO, I WAS JUST AN OBSTACLE BETWEEN YOU AND THE BALL. I UNDERSTAND, BANDY. NOW I'VE GOT NEWS FOR ALL OF YOU.

WE ARE GOING TO VIENNA TO PLAY THEM IN THE EUROPEAN CUP SEMI-FINAL. THE RETURN MATCH WILL BE HERE, OF COURSE.

HOT STUFF. I'VE ALWAYS WANTED TO SEE THE VIENNA STATE HORSES.

Later at Nether Pressley farm.

I'VE BEEN PICKED TO PLAY IN AUSTRIA, MISTER BOYD, CAN I GO?

OF COURSE, WILLIE. YOU KNOW YOU CAN GET AWAY FOR ANY BIG GAME.

Some days later in Vienna.

BANDY ALWAYS LOOKS AS IF HIS CLOTHES ARE TOO BIG!

HE GOT THAT BLAZER MADE THAT SIZE, ROBIN. SAYS HE LIKES ROOM IN HIS CLOTHES!

Next day. I'LL ASK THE BOSS IF I CAN SNEAK ALONG TO THE STABLES TONIGHT. WE DON'T PLAY TILL TOMORROW.

ALL RIGHT, BANDY, YOU CAN GO AND SEE THE HORSES BUT ROBIN WOODFUL WILL GO WITH YOU. WE CAN'T HAVE YOU GETTING LOST!

THANKS, MISTER SIMS. ROBIN WILL ENJOY HIMSELF.

So Wee Bandy and England's centre-half went to see the Vienna State horses.

"You are a hero, Herr Brown!"

WHAT'S UP, BANDY? I THOUGHT YOU WANTED TO SEE THE HORSES.

I SMELL SMOKE, ROBIN. SOMETHING'S BURNING!

FIRE! FIRE! CLEAR THE BUILDING!

LET'S GET OUT OF HERE, BANDY!

TAKE IT EASY, ROBIN.

LEND A HAND WITH THE HORSES...THEY'RE GETTING INTO A PANIC!

COMING OVER, MATE.

WHOA, THERE, BEAUTIES. YOU'LL BE ALL RIGHT IN A MINUTE!

COME BACK, BANDY! YOU'LL BE ROASTED IN THERE!

THIS IS THE LAST ONE. I MUST CALM HIM DOWN.

YOU'VE LOST YOUR EYE-BROWS, HALF YOUR HAIR AND LOOK AT YOUR HANDS. COME TO A DOCTOR.

Some hours later.

YOU ARE A HERO, HERR BROWN. VIENNA SALUTES YOU.

HE'S A HERO WITH BURNED HANDS. NOW WE'LL HAVE TO PLAY VIENNA WITHOUT HIM!

Next evening—

THAT'S TWO-NIL FOR VIENNA. WHY DON'T OUR FORWARDS GET STUCK IN?

Vienna beat Rangers 3-0.

The following week at Pressley.

LOOK, BOSS, THE 'GERS ARE THREE DOWN. LET ME PLAY!

YOUR HANDS HAVEN'T COMPLETELY HEALED YET, BANDY. SORRY.

But Bandy was determined to play in the second leg of the cup-tie. On the night of the match, he shut himself in the boot room.

A BLOKE DOESN'T PLAY FOOTBALL WITH HIS HANDS! RECKON I'LL HAVE TO GRAB MYSELF A GAME! ONCE I'M ON THE PITCH, THEY WON'T BE ABLE TO STOP ME.

A goal in fifteen seconds!

POST BAG PARADE

A ten-shilling postal order is presented to the writer of every letter on this page. A special prize—a pair of ROLLER SKATES or a No. 3 MECCANO SET—also goes to the boys who send in the two star letters of the week. Send YOUR entry to:—

Post Bag Parade
"The Victor"
12 Fetter Lane
Fleet Street
LONDON E.C.4.

When you write to the Editor, please mention your age and the two stories you like best in "The Victor."

Fed 20,000 People

One of the largest pies in the world was made in the village of Denby Dale, Yorkshire, in 1928.

The crust required 80 stones of flour and 16 stones of lard. Meat from seven bullocks was also added. It was baked in a metal dish measuring 15 ft. by 5 ft. Altogether it weighed about 440 stones and it served about 20,000 people.

—A Postal Order to Jay Geiss, 5 Park Village West, London, N.W.1.

The Stalybridge Infant

Sam Hurst, the Stalybridge Infant, who weighed 16 st. 10 lb., won the British Championship the first time he fought in the prize-ring. In his second fight, Hurst lost the crown to Jem Mace—a man 5½ st. lighter —and that was the end of his career.

—A Postal Order to Thomas Herron, 1 Church View, Kimblesworth, Durham.

First Parachutist

To Andre Jacques Garnerin is accorded the honour of being the first person to desend by parachute from a balloon. Garnerin constructed a sort of elongated umbrella twenty-three feet in diameter beneath which a small basket was suspended and, on October 22, 1797, he ascended in a balloon from the Park of Monceau, near Paris. When a height of about 3000 feet had

been reached, Garnerin released the parachute which plunged towards the ground. Fortunately it opened more fully and the rapid descent was checked. He floated to the ground to receive the acclamation of a large crowd.

—A Postal Order to Wladmiar Badz, 15 Somerset Crescent, Melksham, Wiltshire.

Star Letter

Leland Laviose was sent to hospital after he had accidentally shot himself in the foot with a shotgun.

When he was discharged a few weeks later, he demonstrated to friends how he had accidentally almost blown off his foot. Minutes later he was back in hospital after shooting himself in the other foot!

—A Postal Order and Special Prize to Michael Watts, 4 Eve Road, Tottenham, London, N.17.

Largest Aircraft

The largest aircraft ever constructed was the Hughes Hercules flying-boat, which was raised a few feet into the air in a test run in Los Angeles Harbour, California, U.S.A., in November 1947. The eight-engined, 190-ton aircraft had a wing span of 320 feet and a length of 219 feet. It never again flew.

—A Postal Order to Malcolm Brown, 59 Hercules Road, Hellesdon, Norwich, Norfolk.

First International

The first international between England and Scotland was played on a Glasgow cricket ground in 1872. All the Scottish team came from Queen's Park and the result was a goalless draw.

—A Postal Order to John Elliot, 1 Nightingale Place, The Murch, Dinas Powis, Glamorgan, Wales.

Record Holder

The Bell X-2 is the holder of the unofficial speed and altitude records. This swept-wing research plane has streaked through space at 1900 m.p.h. and climbed as high as 126,000 feet (nearly 24 miles). The Bell X-2, with a full speed of 2500 m.p.h., has only a one-man crew.

—A Postal Order to Gerald O'Connell, 19 Oxford Street, Blyth, Northumberland.

Wanted His Dinner

In Mexico City there was chaos in a tram when a shot rang out. The tram screeched to a halt and the driver was found to be shot dead.

When the police arrived and started questioning people, a passenger admitted to shooting the driver. His reason? The driver had gone past his stop without letting him off and he wanted his dinner!

—A Postal Order to Ray Goodall, 10 Webb Lane, Off Hall Street, Stockport, Cheshire.

Handy Haircut

When Pascal Perez, the former world fly-weight champion, was fighting as an amateur in the 1948 Olympics, he was slightly overweight just before his fight. After having a haircut he had shed enough weight to make the limit. Perez won that fight and went on to win a gold medal.

—A Postal Order to Graham Paterson, 35 Shields Avenue, Northville, Bristol, 7.

Judge Was A Bull

A court of appeal was established in Egypt about 2000 B.C. The chief judge was a bull. The decision given in the court was always in favour of the person from whom the bull took food, when offered it by both parties.

—A Postal Order to Maurice Eny, 31 Glencorse Street, Tokoroa, North Island, New Zealand.

Sharp-Shooting Soldiers

One of the greatest battles in the history of the Redmen was fought on August 2, 1867, when 1500 Sioux and Cheyennes fought 32 United States troops at Fort Phil Kearny, Wyoming. The Indians were defeated because, for the first time in Indian warfare, the soldiers used quick-firing Springfield rifles.

—A Postal Order to John Daires, 4 Wykey Cottages, Ruyton XI Towns, Shropshire.

The Laziest Feeder

A small crab that lives on the Great Barrier Reef has an odd way of catching food. When hungry, it seizes an anemone and holds it aloft. When the anemone catches a titbit in its waving tentacles, the crab quickly takes the morsel, eats it, and holds the anemone aloft for more. He continues to do so until he is fully fed.

—A Postal Order to "Victor Reader," 5 Meadow Close, Shirley, Solihull, Warks.

An interesting letter or postcard to the Editor can win two big prizes!

Calcutta Cup

The Calcutta Cup is a rugby cup with a strange story. Competed for annually between Scotland and England, the Calcutta Cup is unlike any other sporting trophy because it is made of melted money.

In India in 1878, the Calcutta Rugby Club was disbanded because of lack of fixtures. The members decided to put the club's funds to good use in the interests of rugby. The funds were exchanged for 500 silver rupees, and Indian silversmiths were commissioned to melt down the coins and make a trophy from them. Famed for their craftsmanship, the silversmiths did a splendid job, and the Calcutta Cup was the result.

—A Postal Order to Michael Calley, 45 Llewellyn Road, Penllergaer, Nr. Swansea, Glamorgan, South Wales.

★ ★ ★ ★

Horse Racing

Horse racing goes back a long way. It is recorded that the earliest race in this country took place about 210 A.D. at Netherby in Yorkshire. The Roman Emperor, visiting Britain, was responsible. Horse racing became fashionable in King Henry II's reign. The track was situated where the famous Smithfield meat market is now.

—A Postal Order to Thomas Curran, 14 Lintie Road, Newarthill, Lanarkshire.

★ ★ ★ ★

The Dead Sea

The Dead Sea is a lake with no outlet. It is about 1300 feet below sea level, and does not fill up because of the great evaporation from its surface. It receives about six million tons of water daily from the River Jordon, but the Palestine sun draws away the water, leaving the lake so rich in salts that plants and animals cannot live in it.

—A Postal Order to Declan Gilleece, 31 Cadogan Road, Fairview, Dublin, 3, Eire.

★ ★ ★ ★

The Tallest Statue

In the Black Hills of Dakota, U.S.A., Mr Korczak Ziolkowski is spending his life carving a statue out of a mountain. It is a monument to the great Sioux chief, Crazy Horse. When finished, it will stand 563 feet tall — 200 feet higher than St Paul's Cathedral.

—A Postal Order to Robert Daniels, 14 New Road, Water Orton, near Birmingham.

First Flier

One of the first men to fly was an English monk who lived in the 11th century. He strapped a pair of wooden wings to his body and a sort of tailplane to his heels and jumped off a tower at Malmesbury Abbey. He glided down to the ground smoothly until he tried to turn in the air. A gust of wind threw him off balance and he crashed to the ground and was crippled for life.

—A Postal Order to David Munroe, 15 Ardley Close, Ruislip, Middlesex.

★ ★ ★ ★

Fifteen Million

Henry Ford, the founder of the Ford Motor Company, had 15 million Model T Ford cars produced. This is a unique production figure in the history of the automobile.

—A Postal Order to M. L. Brown, 24 Bentcliffe Drive, Leeds, 17, Yorkshire.

★ ★ ★ ★

Shortest Fight

The quickest knockout on record was in ten-and-a-half seconds (including a ten-second count) on September 24, 1946. Al Couture struck Ralph Walton while the latter was adjusting a gum shield in his corner, knocking him out.

If the time was accurately taken, it is clear that Couture must have been more than half-way across the ring from his own corner at the opening bell.

—A Postal Order to M. D. Hollington, 38 Maiden Lane, Langley Green, Crawley, Sussex.

★ ★ ★ ★

Great Jumper

The greatest distance jumped by a frog, in an official contest, is 16 feet 10 inches (aggregate of three jumps). This great jump was made by Lucky, owned by Roy Weiner, at Angles Camp, California, on May 24, 1954.

—A Postal Order to Keith Marshall, 171 North Road, Darlington, Co. Durham.

★ ★ ★ ★

550 Goals

The first man to score 500 goals in first-class football was Jimmy McGrory, Celtic and Scottish International centre-forward. Between 1932 and 1938, he collected more than 550 goals, 410 of them in league games, a Scottish record.

—A Postal Order to Jim Hamilton, 6 Orchard Street, Renfrew, Scotland.

Scored—By Shirt!

Dr W. G. Grace, the famous cricketer, featured in a strange incident during a Gloucestershire versus Surrey match in 1878. He was running between the wickets when the ball rebounded from the wicketkeeper's gloves and lodged in W. G.'s shirt. Dr Grace ran six runs before the umpire allowed the bowler to fish out the ball.

—A Postal Order to A. Graham, 18 Monkton Hall Place, Musselburgh, Midlothian.

★ ★ ★ ★

Earthworms

On a good farm, a great number of earthworms work for the farmer by turning over the soil. In many cases, their weight would exceed the weight of the livestock on the farm.

—A Postal Order to Christopher Dedman, Ingleside Farm, Darlington, Co. Durham.

★ ★ ★ ★

Biggest Ever Built

The biggest gun ever built was used by the Germans during World War II. It had a crew of 1000 men and fired three shots an hour. Its barrel was 31 inches in diameter and over 100 feet long. The weight of the gun and carriage was 1300 tons.

—A Postal Order to Alan Phillips, 1 Park View, Lynsted, near Sittingbourne, Kent.

No Trouble

Fans in Addis Ababa (Ethiopia) must pay a small deposit as well as their admission money, to enter football grounds. If the match ends without trouble, they get their money back. It's reported matches are played under ideal conditions.

—Michael O'Brien, 37 Southdown Road, Sandfields Estate, Port Talbot, Glam.

★ ★ ★ ★

Band On Bikes

In Holland, there is a military band which parades the streets on bikes. The soldiers have to keep their eyes on the road ahead and also on the music. One hand plays the instrument and the other grips the handlebars. Imagine the chaos there would be if one bike crashed into another.

—A Postal Order to S. A. Turner, 5 Shannon Ct., Dynevor Road, London, N.16.

★ ★ ★ ★

A Drop In The Ocean

Can you imagine 3,500,000 cubic feet of water? I don't expect you can, but this is the amount of water that the Amazon River pours into the Atlantic Ocean every second!

—A Postal Order to Paul Smith, 22 Weller House, George Road, Dockhead, London, S.E.16.

Star Letter

On January 6, 1918, Captain J. H. Hedley was an observer in a plane which was attacked over the German lines. As his pilot dived, Hedley was thrown out, without a parachute.

He fell for several hundred feet, then landed on the tail of the plane he had just left, and was brought to the ground safely.

—A Postal Order and Special Prize to J. W. Waddell, 14 Gartland Road, Grindon, Sunderland, Co. Durham.

Slow But Sure

The record for the slowest century in first-class cricket is held by D. J. McGlew of South Africa in a match against Australia at Durban in season 1957-58. McGlew took 9 hours 5 minutes to hit a hundred runs.

—A Postal Order to David Money, St Gilbert's School, Hartlebury, near Kidderminster, Worcs.

Gate Money—1s 8d

Luton F.C. have come a long way since December 6, 1930, when they played a league match (Third Division) against Thames before a "crowd" of only 469. After routine expenses had been deducted, Luton's share of the gate worked out at 1s 8d.

—A Postal Order to Paul Tubbs, Cranley, 111 Marlpit Lane, Old Coulsdon, Surrey.

Two Lancasters go down in flames and fourteen British aircrew die—because Mandeville refused to listen to Braddock!

I FLEW WITH BRADDOCK

ALL AIR CREWS REPORT TO THE BRIEFING ROOM IMMEDIATELY.

RIGHT, LADS, THAT'S ENOUGH DINGHY DRILL FOR THE TIME BEING. WE'D BETTER GET OVER TO THE BRIEFING.

Sergeant Matt Braddock, V.C., was the greatest pilot of the last war. This is the story of the famous book about him, written by George Bourne, his navigator. Braddock and the crew of F Fox, his Lancaster, were sent to Barminster R.A.F. station to take part in a special mission, the dropping of a big, new bomb designed by Mr Smith, a brilliant scientist. The commanding officer at Barminster was Group Captain Mandeville, whose big reputation Braddock considered phoney.

MEN, WE'VE GOT TO START TRAINING IN LOW-LEVEL FLIGHTS FOR A SPECIAL JOB. OUR FIRST PRACTICE FLIGHT WILL BE TOMORROW MORNING. THE NAVIGATION OFFICER WILL GIVE YOU THE DETAILS OF THE ROUTE.

TOMORROW, YOU'LL FLY IN THREES OVER A TRIANGULAR COURSE OF TWO HUNDRED MILES AT A HEIGHT OF 300 FEET. THE FIRST COURSE WILL BE EAST.

ARE YOU EXPECTING TROUBLE ON THIS FLIGHT?

THE FLIGHT ISN'T BEING LAID ON TO GIVE YOU AN ARMCHAIR RIDE, BRADDOCK.

I'M NOT LOOKING FOR AN ARM-CHAIR RIDE, BUT THE GENIUS WHO WORKED OUT THIS FLIGHT HAS FORGOTTEN ABOUT THE SUN. FOR THE FIRST LEG, WE'LL HAVE THE SUN SMACK IN OUR EYES, AND AT LOW LEVEL, THAT'S DANGEROUS!

WE COULD EASILY REVERSE THE FLIGHT PLAN, SIR.

THIS ISN'T A PEACE-TIME PICNIC. THE RISKS MUST NOT BE EXAGGERATED. THE FLIGHT PLAN WON'T BE CHANGED FOR THE SAKE OF BRADDOCK'S EYES.

Next morning.

LOOK OUT, BRAD. THE WING TIPS ARE NEARLY TOUCHING!

THAT'S OKAY, HAM, I'VE TAKEN EVASIVE ACTION. FORMATION FLYING INTO THE SUN AT THIS HEIGHT IS A BIT DODGY. HOW ARE THE OTHERS DOING, REAR-GUNNER?

TWO OF THEM HAVE COLLIDED, SKIPPER! THEY'VE CRASHED IN FLAMES!

After the collision, the rest of the exercise was completed successfully and the Lancs returned to base.

"Mandeville has a lot to answer for!"

WHO CRASHED, JIM?

BILL DAVIES AND JOE PENTON. THEY WERE BOTH EXPERIENCED PILOTS. BOTH HAVE DONE A FULL TOUR. I RECKON THE SUN GLARE IN THEIR EYES MUST HAVE CAUSED IT.

MANDEVILLE HAS A LOT TO ANSWER FOR!

That afternoon in the sergeants' mess, Bourne talked to Lawrie Laneman, a sergeant in the orderly room.

THAT WAS A BAD SHOW THIS MORNING. TWO PLANES AND FOURTEEN MEN WIPED OUT.

THE SUN GLARE WAS BLINDING.

EVERYONE KNOWS THAT BRADDOCK SPOKE ABOUT SUN GLARE AT THE BRIEFING, BUT THE C.O. IS PASSING THE BUCK AS USUAL. HE'S BLAMING THE CRASH ON PENTON. HE WAS AN ACE PILOT BY ALL ACCOUNTS, BUT YOU WOULDN'T THINK IT TO READ MANDEVILLE'S REPORT.

THAT'S TYPICAL OF MANDEVILLE!

Later.

YOU KNOW, GEORGE, MANDEVILLE IS ONE OF THE CLEVEREST MEN I'VE EVER MET. HE'S BEEN IN THE R.A.F. FOR YEARS AND THEY'VE NEVER FOUND HIM OUT. HE'S NEVER TO BLAME FOR ANYTHING. WHEN SOMETHING GOES WRONG, SOMEONE ELSE CAUSED IT—NEVER HIM!

WHAT ABOUT THAT DUD SHOT WITH THE BIG BOMB?

Mandeville had insisted on dropping the first of Mr Smith's test bombs — and almost hit the Royal train!

HE WRIGGLED OUT OF THAT ALL RIGHT. THEY FOUND DEFECTS IN HIS BOMB-SIGHT AND ALTIMETER.

Next morning, another practice flight was arranged.

HULLO, GEORGE. HEY, WHAT ARE YOU DOING IN FLYING KIT? HASN'T MANDEVILLE TOLD YOU ABOUT THE SIGNAL HE RECEIVED FROM GROUP?

NO. WHAT SIGNAL IS THIS?

IT SAID THAT BRADDOCK AND HIS CREW WERE TO BE TAKEN OFF ALL OPERATIONS UNTIL FURTHER NOTICE.

FIRST WE'VE HEARD OF IT. BUT I'D BETTER HURRY OR BRAD WILL SLAY ME. WAIT TILL I TELL HIM ABOUT THIS!

NOT SO FAST, BRAD. I'VE SOMETHING TO TELL YOU.

NOT JUST NOW, GEORGE. HURRY UP. IT'S NEAR TAKE-OFF TIME.

F684

The signal said "Stop"—but it takes more than a signal to stop Matt Braddock!

CONTINUED ON PAGE 97 F Fox takes a pounding from the German defences and lands Mandeville in hot water!

The crowds flock to see Gorgeous Gus—the player who packs the hardest sock in soccer!

GORGEOUS GUS

The Earl of Boote bought Redburn Rovers, a First Division football club, and played centre-forward for them. The earl was at once nicknamed Gorgeous Gus by the fans, because of his immaculate appearance, but he proved to have the hardest shot ever seen in soccer! Gus refused to run for the ball—with his shot he demanded perfect passes. He signed a new star team for Rovers, regardless of expense. One morning, Jenkins, Gorgeous Gus's butler, came to see Sam Hopkins, Rovers' manager, at the ground.

GOOD MORNING, MR HOPKINS. THE MASTER'S COMPLIMENTS, AND THIS IS THE TEAM FOR SATURDAY. THERE WILL BE NO CHANGES.

I'M AFRAID THERE WILL, JENKINS. THAT WAS WEBB'S DOCTOR ON THE PHONE. WEBB WON'T BE FIT, SO WE'RE SHORT OF A LEFT WINGER.

THE MASTER WILL BE SORRY TO HEAR ABOUT WEBB AND HE'LL DECIDE WHO IS TO TAKE HIS PLACE.

POOR OLD WEBB. I RECKON HE'S FINISHED NOW. THE MASTER WILL SIGN ANOTHER BIG STAR AND WEBB WON'T PLAY IN THE FIRST TEAM AGAIN.

But Webb had his own ideas about Saturday's match.

WHAT'S THE IDEA, WEBB? I ORDERED YOU TO STAY IN BED.

I'M ALL RIGHT. I'VE GOT TO BE. IF I DON'T PLAY TOMORROW, GORGEOUS GUS WILL SIGN ON SOME STAR AND I'LL NEVER GET MY PLACE BACK.

IT WON'T WORK, WEBB. IF YOU PLAY TOMORROW, YOU'LL PROBABLY FINISH YOUR CAREER FOR GOOD.

PARDON ME IF I INTRUDE.

IT—IT'S GORGEOUS GUS!

I CAME TO SEE HOW YOU WERE, WEBB, AND I COULDN'T HELP OVERHEARING. I ASSURE YOU, YOU'VE NOTHING TO WORRY ABOUT. I SHALL FIND A CAPABLE SUBSTITUTE, BUT, WHENEVER YOU'RE FIT, THE FIRST TEAM PLACE IS YOURS. BUT FIRST WE'VE GOT TO GET YOU FIT. DO YOU THINK AN OCEAN VOYAGE IN THE SUN WOULD DO HIM GOOD, DOCTOR?

IT WOULD BE JUST THE THING TO GET HIM ON HIS FEET AGAIN, IF IT COULD BE ARRANGED. BUT IT WOULD COST A FORTUNE!

Gorgeous Gus sent Tim Webb and his family away on a cruise on his private yacht. Full wages were paid to Webb, and his place in the team was guaranteed when he had regained his fitness. When news of this leaked out, Gus's popularity with the players fairly zoomed.

Next day, on the way to play Livermere.

I RECKON WE'LL MURDER LIVERMERE. ALL WE'VE GOT TO DO IS GET THE BALL TO GORGEOUS GUS.

YES, HE'S THE BOY, YOU KNOW, WHEN I FIRST SET EYES ON GUS, I DIDN'T LIKE HIM. HE LOOKED TOO TOFFEE-NOSED FOR ME, BUT AFTER WHAT HE DID FOR TIM WEBB, I'LL PUNCH ANYONE ON THE NOSE WHO SAYS A WORD AGAINST HIM!

LOOK AT THAT. LAST YEAR WHEN WE PLAYED LIVERMERE, THERE WAS A CROWD OF ONLY 20,000. GORGEOUS GUS FAIRLY DRAWS IN THE CROWDS!

YES, SPECTACULAR SHOOTING ALWAYS HAS THEM ROLLING UP.

68

The butler on the wing.

The flashing foot of the Earl of Boote.

Livermere hit back, and equalised with a lucky goal.

Bull Rawlings kept his word. The dirtiest player in football stopped at nothing to halt the Rovers' attacks.

A job for the dirtiest player in football!

WOW! HE NEARLY HAD THE LEGS OFF ME!

GOAL! A REAL DAISY-CUTTER IF EVER I SAW ONE!

A few minutes later, the butler served the ball up on a plate to Gus.

OVER TO YOU, MASTER.

THANK YOU, JENKINS.

NOT THIS TIME, BOSS. HE'S GOING BACK TO THE CENTRE. LOOKS LIKE HE'S STAYING TO THE END.

GREAT GOAL. GUS WILL WALK OFF NOW. HE CONSIDERS HE'S DONE HIS DUTY WHEN HE SCORES TWO OR THREE GOALS, AND HE WALKS OFF!

Gorgeous Gus stayed to the end of the game. There was no further scoring, and Rovers won 3-1. As they trooped off the field, the Redburn players got the shock of their lives, when Gus spoke to Bull Rawlings.

I SAY, MY MAN, WOULD YOU LIKE TO SIGN ON FOR THE ROVERS?

I'D LIKE IT FINE. I'M FED UP WITH LIVERMERE. THEY DON'T APPRECIATE ME HERE.

VERY WELL, MY MAN. I SHALL ARRANGE YOUR TRANSFER IMMEDIATELY. WE WILL SIGN THE PAPERS IN A FEW MINUTES. YOU WILL REPORT TO REDBURN ON TUESDAY MORNING.

DID YOU HEAR THAT? GUS IS SIGNING ON THAT DIRTY BRUTE!

DON'T WORRY! THE MASTER'S WAYS ARE SOMETIMES STRANGE, BUT THEY HAVE MUCH MERIT!

On Tuesday.

I'LL MAKE A BIG DIFFERENCE TO THIS TEAM. YOU'RE A BUNCH OF NAMBIE PAMBIES. NOW YOU'LL SEE A REAL PLAYER!

WHY YOU—

STEADY! HERE COMES GUS.

AH, MY MAN. I WAS HOPING TO GET HERE BEFORE YOU AND SAVE YOU THE TROUBLE OF CHANGING. THERE IS NO NEED FOR YOU TO BE IN FOOTBALL KIT. KINDLY GO AND CHANGE INTO YOUR ORDINARY CLOTHES.

WELL, IF THAT'S THE WAY YOU WANT IT, IT SUITS ME. I DON'T NEED AS MUCH TRAINING AS THESE OTHER GUYS.

A few minutes later.

TAKE THIS, MY MAN! WE PAID £20,000 FOR YOUR TRANSFER, NOW EARN YOUR KEEP! YOU WILL TAKE THESE IMPLEMENTS AND GO ROUND THE GROUND PICKING UP EVERY PIECE OF PAPER. I EXPECT TO SEE THE GROUND AS CLEAN AS A PIN. THAT WILL BE YOUR DUTY FROM NOW ON!

YOU CAN'T INSULT ME LIKE THIS! I'M A FOOTBALL PLAYER, NOT A SCAVENGER!

YOU'RE NO FOOTBALL PLAYER, RAWLINGS, YOU'RE A SAVAGE. I OBTAINED YOUR TRANSFER TO STOP YOU DEGRADING THE NOBLE GAME OF FOOTBALL. I ASSURE YOU, YOU WON'T GET A TRANSFER TO ANOTHER CLUB. YOU'LL PICK UP THE LITTER AROUND HERE OR YOU'LL GET NO WAGES!

LOOKS LIKE I'VE NO CHOICE!

WELL, WHAT DO YOU KNOW! GUS PAID OUT £20,000 JUST TO STOP BULL RAWLINGS PLAYING FOOTBALL. THERE'S NEVER BEEN A SURPRISE PACKET LIKE GORGEOUS GUS!

CONTINUED ON PAGE 100 Gus sets a referee a tricky problem when he uproots the goal with a terrific shot!

A hunter sets a trap—and Morgyn falls right into it!

SEVEN TRAILS TO MORGYN THE MIGHTY

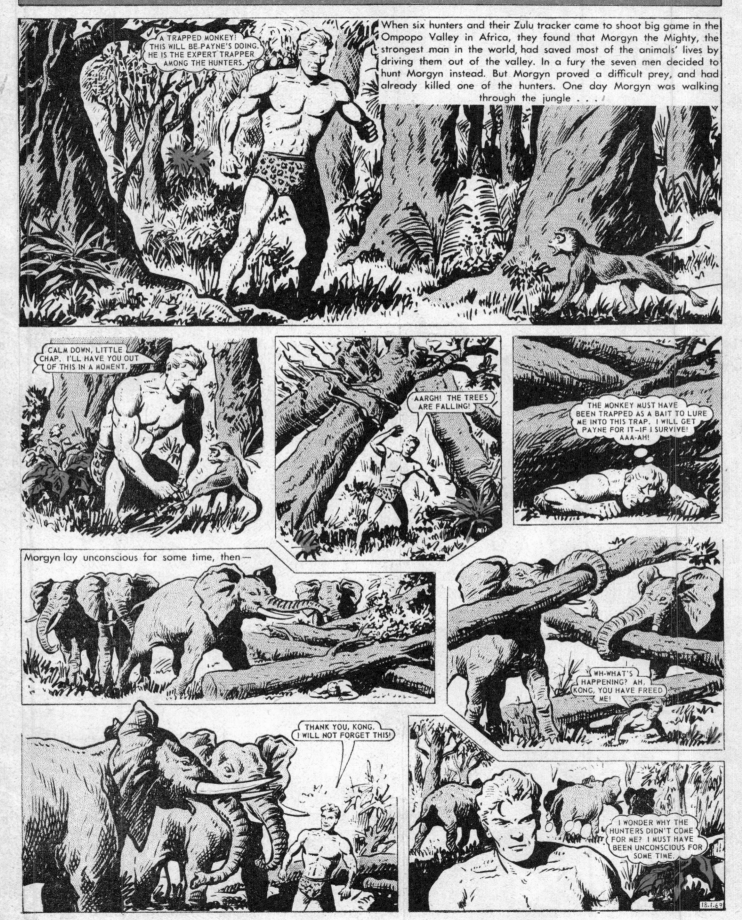

"The demon white man has struck."

Some time later —

HE'S ESCAPED FROM THE TRAP. HOW COULD HE MANAGE? EVEN MORGYN COULDN'T HAVE MOVED THOSE TREE TRUNKS.

HAH! IT COULD NOT HAVE BEEN A VERY GOOD TRAP.

I HAVE AT LEAST SHOWN HE CAN BE CAUGHT. TOMORROW I WILL GO OUT AND FINISH HIM FOR GOOD!

Later —

SO THEY'VE BUILT A BARRIER TO PROTECT THEMSELVES. I'LL SOON SHOW THEM THAT A PUNY THING LIKE THAT WON'T MAKE THEM SAFE!

THIS WILL SHOW THEM EXACTLY HOW SAFE THEY ARE.

THEY'LL GET THE SHOCK OF THEIR LIVES WHEN THEY SEE THIS!

AAH! LOOK! THE DEMON WHITE MAN HAS STRUCK AGAIN. WE MUST TELL BWANA PACKARD.

BWANA, THE FENCE IS DOWN. THE DEMON WHITE MAN HAS STRUCK.

WHAT? HE MUST BE STOPPED.

HOW CAN WE GET HIM?

I WILL GO OUT TOMORROW AND SET A TRAP FOR HIM. THAT WILL FINISH HIM FOR GOOD!

GOOD IDEA, PAYNE. I'M SURE EVEN HE WON'T BE ABLE TO ESCAPE YOUR TRAP AGAIN.

ACH, YES! THEN HE WILL TROUBLE US NO MORE.

HMPH! THAT'S WHAT THEY THINK!

Morgyn lays a trap!

Payne was left in the kind of trap he had used so often on helpless animals. When the other hunters eventually found him he was completely unnerved and had to return to America. Morgyn had reduced the odds to five to one against!

CONTINUED ON PAGE 103 Morgyn's life is saved —— by a little monkey!

EXCITING PICTURE STORIES THAT THRILL — IN A PAPER EVERY BOY WILL ENJOY!

THE VICTOR

EVERY MONDAY

Price 4½d

No. 12
MAY 13th
1961

SEPHTON STAYED AT HIS POST!

In May 1941, the British hospital ship Aba was attacked in the Mediterranean by German dive-bombers. The Red Cross markings on the fore and aft decks were no protection. Unarmed and helpless, the Aba was mercilessly bombed.

THE NAZI BRUTES. THEY MUST HAVE SEEN OUR RED CROSS MARKINGS YET STILL THEY BOMB US. SEND OUT AN SOS.

RADIO ROOM

IT'S THE HOSPITAL SHIP, ABA, SIR. SHE'S BEING ATTACKED BY DIVE BOMBERS!

CONTINUED ON BACK PAGE

CONTINUED FROM FRONT PAGE The cruiser "Coventry" picked up the SOS and raced to the rescue.

ACHTUNG! A BRITISH CRUISER. THAT'S A MORE VALUABLE TARGET THAN A HOSPITAL SHIP.

LEADER CALLING! LEAVE THE OTHER SHIP. ATTACK THE CRUISER! TARGET COMING UP, FIVE DEGREES STARBOARD!

In one of the Coventry's gun-direction towers, Petty Officer Alfred Sephton directed the guns.

Although in great pain and bleeding heavily from a mortal wound, Sephton stayed at his post directing deadly accurate gunfire at the enemy planes.

GOOD SHOOTING, 'A' BATTERY. NEW TARGETS COMING UP TO PORT. STAND BY!

The anti-aircraft fire took a terrible toll of the German dive-bombers, and they finally turned tail.

The battle won, Sephton at last left his vital post. He was rushed to the ship's hospital but died next day. Sephton had sacrificed his life to save the Coventry and the Aba. He was awarded the Victoria Cross.

SEE PAGE 114 for the next colour cover story.

PRINTED AND PUBLISHED IN GREAT BRITAIN BY D. C. THOMSON & CO., LTD., AND JOHN LENG & CO., LTD., 12 FETTER LANE, FLEET STREET, LONDON, E.C.4. REGISTERED FOR TRANSMISSION BY CANADIAN MAGAZINE POST. © D. C. THOMSON & CO., LTD., 1961.

Two mile races within minutes of each other! Most athletes would refuse to run—but not Alf Tupper!

THE TOUGH OF THE TRACK

" Try to break four minutes for the mile!"

" I'll leave him standing!"

CONTINUED ON PAGE 105 Alf changes his address — and misses his invitation to run in the European Games!

Ching Paw, a Burmese boy, wanted to kill Japs—and not even the British Army was going to stop the fighting fifteen-year-old!

The FORGOTTEN FOURTEENTH

IN Burma during World War Two, many natives joined the ranks of the "forgotten" men of the British Fourteenth Army. Young Ching Paw enlisted in a very unusual way.

WELL, THAT'S THE LOT. YOU'VE GOT ALL YOUR SUPPLIES NOW?

YES, THANKS. THERE'LL BE NO AIRSTRIPS WHERE WE'RE GOING. IF WE WANT ANYTHING IN THE JUNGLE, IT WILL HAVE TO BE DROPPED BY PARACHUTE.

EVERYTHING CLEARED, SIR!

RIGHT-HO, SERGEANT, WE'LL MOVE OFF NOW.

The trucks roared deep into the jungle

. . . then when the track petered out, the loads were transferred to mules.

At an infantry battalion H.Q.—

RIGHT, MAXON—LET'S HAVE THAT ONE OPEN.

JUMPING TAD-POLES!

WHAT'S WRONG, MAXON?

A NATIVE NIPPER! WHAT THE DICKENS IS HE DOING AT THE FRONT LINE?

I CHING PAW. ME VERY GOOD FIGHTING MAN. YOU GIVING ME WEAPONS—ME KILLING PLENTY JAPOONS.

Captain Summers was called over.

WHAT ARE WE GOING TO DO WITH HIM? WE CAN'T SEND HIM BACK, BECAUSE WE HAVE NO CONTACT WITH ANYBODY.

ME COMING IN BOX, SAHIB OFFICER. MAKING LONG JOURNEY IN STOMACH OF IRON EAGLE.

WE CAN'T TURN HIM LOOSE, SIR, SO WE'LL JUST HAVE TO TAKE HIM WITH US. BETTER LEAVE HIM WITH ME IN THE REAR ECHELON. I'LL SOON FIND HIM A JOB.

Ching Paw, the little native boy, became the mascot of the battalion

. . . and Quartermaster Shaw found him plenty of jobs to do.

Alone—against the Japs!

SAHIB SHAW, ALL THIS IS WOMANS' WORK. I COMING TO KILL JAPOONS.

YOU'RE TOO LITTLE, CHING PAW. YOU WAIT UNTIL YOU'RE A MAN.

THIS WORKING IS NOT FOR ME. I JUST TAKE ONE RIFLE AND SOME AMMUNITION AND GO FINDING JAPOONS TO SLAY.

Ching Paw waited until nightfall to put his plan into operation.

Next morning.

I HEARING SOMEONE'S ON TRAIL. BETTER ME HIDE.

JAPOONS! MARCHING TOWARDS MY FRIENDS! ME MUST RETURN AND GIVE THE ALARM!

MORE. JAPOONS!

Ching Paw dashed back into the cover of the jungle.

Back at the British camp, the shot had been heard.

QUARTERMASTER, THAT SHOT WE HEARD, IT WAS JAPS—SCORES OF 'EM, AND ALL HEADING THIS WAY.

WE'LL PULL OUT. THERE'S NO USE STOPPING HERE—WE CAN'T HOLD THEM OFF ANYWAY!

WE'LL LEAVE THAT STUFF WHERE IT IS. THERE'S A CHANCE THE JAPS MAY MISS THE CAMP ALTOGETHER.

I HAVE FOOLED THE JAPOONS. THIS TRACK WILL BE TAKING ME BACK TO CAMP.

QUARTERMASTER SAHIB! QUARTERMASTER SHAW! WHERE ARE YOU?

THEY ALL HAVING GONE. NOW JAPOONS COMING—TAKING ALL VALUABLE! THINGS BELONGING TO QUARTERMASTER SAHIB.

" When greedy jackal gorges himself, he forgets to keep watch for the hunter!"

I MUST GOING FIND FRIENDS— BUT NO, CRATE GIVES ME BETTER IDEA!

PUT BOX RIGHT WAY UP, FIRST.

THEN MAKE LITTLE SURPRISE FOR YELLOW JAPOONS.

OLD SHIRTS WILL HIDE—AND SURPRISE NEARLY READY.

BANZAI! HERE IS MOST EXCELLENT LOOT FOR HONOURABLE NIPPON SOLDIERS.

AIEE! ONLY JUST IN TIME WAS I. JAPOON JACKALS COMING NOW.

WHAT HAS HONOURABLE COMRADE FOUND?

ONLY SHIRTS OF DESPICABLE BRITISH!

COME HERE—MOST EXCELLENT WHITE SUGAR.

WHEN GREEDY JACKAL GORGES HIMSELF, HE FORGETS TO KEEP WATCH FOR THE HUNTER!

Hearing the explosions, the British troops, with reinforcements, dashed back to their camp.

THE NIPPER HAS SAVED THE WHOLE QUARTERMASTER'S STORES. THREE CHEERS FOR CHING. HIP–HIP—

HURRAH!

WELL, I SLEW SOME JAPOONS AFTER ALL!

CONTINUED ON PAGE 145   Major Peter S. Mills joins the 14th Army —— with the impact of a tornado!

The boyhood story in pictures of Britain's ace of speed.

WHEN HE WAS A BOY
STIRLING MOSS

BRITAIN'S FOREMOST RACING DRIVER, STIRLING MOSS, HAS DRIVEN ALL THE WORLD'S FASTEST CARS ON ALL THE MOST FAMOUS CIRCUITS. "MR. MOTOR-RACING," AS HIS FELLOW DRIVERS CALL HIM, HAS WON EVERY CLASSIC RACE AND BEEN BRITISH MOTOR-RACING CHAMPION NINE TIMES.

At the age of 3, Stirling was already speed-mad. On his tricycle, he was a constant worry to his parents.

STIRLING, FOR GOODNESS' SAKE— NOT SO FAST!

When Stirling was five, his father employed a gym instructor to see that his son kept fit.

At 6, Stirling went to kindergarten. He didn't like lessons much and was often in trouble for daydreaming.

GAZING AT CARS INSTEAD OF PAYING ATTENTION TO LESSONS AGAIN, STIRLING! THIS WILL HAVE TO STOP!

He was still very young when his father taught him the first essentials of driving in the driveway of their home at Tring, in Buckinghamshire.

Thanks to his father's insistence on plenty of P.T., Stirling was a very agile boy. He enjoyed playing "Tarzan" in the woods on the family farm.

But he soon found that this game could be rather dangerous.

HELP! QUICK, HELP!

His first race—and he breaks the course record!

But this agility was useful at school, where sport was rapidly becoming his best subject.

While on holiday at his father's farm, Stirling would spend most of his time on horseback—riding fast, of course.

Stirling was only 11 when he was given his first car—an ancient 7 h.p. saloon.

WELL, IT'S ALL YOURS, SON—BUT BE CAREFUL.

He spent hours driving round a rough circuit on the farm.

In the years that followed, Stirling learned everything his father, a skilled amateur mechanic, could teach him about engines.

And by the time he was 16, he had decided on his future career.

I'VE MADE UP MY MIND. I'M GOING TO BE A RACING DRIVER.

At 18, Stirling was able to buy his first racing car, a 500 c.c. Cooper. He could hardly wait for it to be built.

IS IT NEARLY FINISHED YET?

NOT QUITE, LAD, JUST BE PATIENT.

As soon as the car was completed, Stirling entered for the classic Shelsley Walsh hill climb. But he was doomed to disappointment.

THEY HAVEN'T ACCEPTED MY ENTRY!

However, he soon had his chance, on the Prescott hill climb, where he came in fourth, and set up a new course record.

A month later, Stirling Moss wore his first victor's wreath when he won another hill climb, at Stamner Park. Since then, he has gone from victory to victory to become Britain's No. 1 driver, and one of the greatest-ever names in world racing.

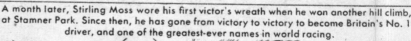

SEE PAGE 128 for When He Was a Boy: Denis Law

POST BAG PARADE

No Sense Of Humour

A playful airline pilot was suspended for 30 days because he walked up and down in front of the passenger ticket line reading a book plainly marked, "How To Fly In Ten Easy Lessons."

—A Postal Order to Peter Halkyard, 18 Aldesworth Road, Cantley, 2, Doncaster.

* * * *

Strange Save

During a pre-war Scottish League match between Hearts and Celtic, an amazing thing happened. Celtic were on the attack and the left-winger centred the ball. Jimmy McGrory, Celtic centre-forward, leapt to head the ball in a horizontal position about six feet off the ground.

The Hearts goalkeeper, Jack Harkness, saw that McGrory was going to hit his head on the goalpost. Harkness dived, not at the ball, but at McGrory. He managed to push McGrory out of the way of the post and, although McGrory hurt his shoulder, he walked quickly over to Jack Harkness and thanked him.

Surely this is one of the most amazing saves ever made by a goalkeeper.

—A Postal Order to Peter Heslop, 77 Antlers Hill, North Chingford, London, E.4.

* * * *

The Big Show

Charles Cruft, who died in 1938, was the founder of the famous dog show which bears his name. The figure of 86 entries for the first show in 1887 rose in 70 years to the staggering total of 12,681. Yet Mr Cruft himself didn't own a dog. He kept a cat as a pet.

—A Postal Order to Philip Page, 30 Regal Crescent, Ditton, Widnes, Lancs.

This Is *YOUR* Page!

A ten-shilling postal order is presented to the writer of every letter on this page. A special prize —a pair of ROLLER SKATES or a No. 3 MECCANO SET—also goes to the boys who send in the two star letters of the week.

Send YOUR entry to:—
POST BAG PARADE,
"THE VICTOR,"
12 FETTER LANE,
FLEET STREET,
LONDON, E.C.4.

When you write to the Editor, please mention your age and the two stories you like best in "The Victor."

"The Original"

Did you know that the first lifeboat was launched in 1790? It was designed by William Wouldhave and built by Henry Greathead. It was propelled by ten oarsmen and it was aptly name The Original.

—A Postal Order to Terry Shotter, 3 Noke Shot, Harpenden, Herts.

* * * *

Boot Banquet

When the war between Russia and Japan broke out in 1904, a merchant in Moscow said that he would eat his boots if the Japs didn't sue for peace before July. They didn't—so the merchant, true to his promise, ate his strange meal on July 1, 1904.

—A Postal Order to B. Wilkinson, 64 Nursery Road, Davyhulme, Nr. Manchester.

* * * *

Three In One

A Hampshire grocer, fed up with the foxes that kept stealing his chickens, declared war on the raiders. One night he took a gun with him up a tree and lay in wait for the thieves.

At last a fox came along and trotted off with a chicken in its mouth. Before the grocer could fire, another fox appeared and tried to take the other's prize. The grocer fired and, losing his balance, fell out of the tree.

When he picked himself up, he found the two foxes and chicken dead. They were all killed with one cartridge.

—A Postal Order to Steven Dixon, 9 Chelwood Walk, York.

* * * *

On The Boil

Water is almost the worst liquid in the world in which to boil an egg. It takes more gas or electricity to heat it up than does any other common substance. But once it's hot, water takes longer to cool than anything else. So what you lose in your breakfast, you gain on your hot water bottle.

—A Postal Order to Geoffrey Telfer, 43 Granville Avenue, West Hartlepool.

Little Monkey!

The smallest monkey in the world is the six-inch pygmy marmoset, which is found in Brazil. It weighs about half a pound, and can sit comfortably in a spoon!

—A Postal Order to John Broomhead, 59 Kingshill Road, Knowled, Bristol, 4.

* * * *

The Name Is Mud

In Queen Victoria's reign, when the British were fighting in India, the troops' bright red uniforms stood out clearly against the dark land. The soldiers began to cover their uniforms with mud, so that it would act as a camouflage. The Indian word for mud is "khaki."

—A Postal Order to Peter Beaver, 12 Woodberry Avenue, North Harrow, Middlesex.

* * * *

Precious Metal

Today aluminium is one of the cheapest and most useful metals known to man. In the early nineteenth century, however, it cost several hundred shillings a pound because of its rarity. It was so scarce that, in the court of Napoleon III of France, the very highly honoured guests were given aluminium plates, while the lesser important guests had to be content with silver and gold plates.

—A Postal Order to L. Milne, 150 Heathryfold Circle, Aberdeen.

* * * *

Sleepy Head!

An Egyptian desert snail (helix desertorum) came back to life after being gummed to a tablet and exhibited in a glass case in the British Museum for two years (1846-48). Everyone considered the snail to be quite dead, but after its long sleep it awoke to live for a considerable time afterwards.

—A Postal Order to T. Davidson, 4 Penistone Road, Pennywell, Sunderland.

Star Letter

Sound-waves travel at 1120 feet a second, but wireless-waves travel at 300 million metres a second. Thus, anyone at Singapore (8000 miles away) can hear Big Ben on the radio before anyone standing just across the River Thames a few hundred feet from the clock.

—A Postal Order and Special Prize to Graham Elder, 80 Beatty Cres., Kirkcaldy, Fife.

STARTING TODAY:—Meet Crib Carson, a tough young boxer who will use any sly trick or dodge in his fight to get to the top!

CRIB CARSON—*FIGHTER*

Crib Carson was on his way to Liverport's Rink Stadium, where he was to have his sixth professional fight as a middle-weight. His opponent, Tug Williams, at 11 stones 5 pounds, was 10 pounds heavier than Crib and had over a hundred fights to his credit, but the young boxer was determined to collect the winner's purse of three pounds.

I'LL GET WHAT I WANT IN HERE.

THIS IS WHAT YOU ASKED FOR—A SMALL TIN OF WHITE TALCUM POWDER. NINEPENCE, PLEASE.

HERE'S YOUR MONEY.

At the boxers' entrance there were a few old pugs hanging around. They were hoping that some of the boxers on the programme would fail to turn up and that Laz Hart, the promoter, would be forced to use one of them to fill the vacancy.

I AIN'T GOING TO BE LIKE THESE MUGS. THEY'RE LOSERS. I'M GOING TO USE MY WITS TO WIN.

GET A MOVE ON, KID. YOU'RE ON FIRST. TUG'S BEEN HERE TEN MINUTES.

I WON'T TAKE LONG TO GET READY.

IT'LL BE EASY FOR YOU TONIGHT, TUG. THIS KID CARSON'S GOT NO EXPERIENCE.

TUG'S GOT A SHOCK COMING.

NOW FOR SOME FIGHT-WINNING TACTICS.

THESE SHOE-BLACKING SHADOWS MAKE ME LOOK LIKE A REAL SICK MAN.

Crib had just finished his strange preparations when his second arrived to bandage his hands.

WHAT ARE YOU DOING IN THIS SPARE DRESSING ROOM? I'D A JOB TO FIND YOU. YOU'RE ON IN FIVE MINUTES.

I DON'T MUCH LIKE CROWDS.

THAT KID'S GOT A BAD COUGH. HE SHOULDN'T BE FIGHTING.

" What a punch!"

When the fight started, Crib put the final part of his plan into action.

I SHOULDN'T BE FIGHTING. GIVE ME A COUPLE OF ROUNDS BEFORE YOU OUTS ME. I GET NO MONEY IF I'M KAYOED IN THE FIRST.

YOU'RE ON AN EASY THING, TONIGHT, TUG. HE LOOKS IN A BAD WAY ALREADY.

MY PLAN'S WORKING. TUG'S PULLING HIS PUNCHES AND TAKING IT EASY.

Crib then exploded into action.

NAIL HIM, YOUNG 'UN. TUG'S TOO SLOW TO CATCH A COLD.

THE BOY'S A BETTER BOXER THAN TUG, ANYWAY.

WHAT A PUNCH!

THAT'S CURTAINS FOR TUG.

YOU DIRTY DOG! YOU WON BY A TRICK. YOU FOOLED TUG.

HE'S THE MUG! NOT ME!

Crib headed for the gym where he did his training.

NOW TO GET THE PRACTICE I'M NEEDING.

ELLY'S GYM.

I HAVEN'T GOT THESE JABS RIGHT. I DIDN'T HIT HIM HARD ENOUGH WITH THE FIRST ONE.

HERE'S YOUR THREE QUID, KID. I HEAR YOU PULLED A FAST ONE ON TUG.

THERE'S NO LAW AGAINST IT. I NEVER FOULED HIM. AND IT'LL COST YOU MORE TO GET ME FOR MY NEXT FIGHT, LAZ.

"I hope you get bashed!"

I MUST GET MORE POWER INTO MY LEFT JABS.

PACK IT IN, CRIB. I WANT TO LOCK UP.

I AIN'T HAD ENOUGH PRACTICE YET, KELLY. YOU GO ON HOME. I'LL LOCK UP.

A fortnight later, Crib was due to fight in another Hart Promotion at the Rink. His opponent was Eddie Acton of Leeds, a clever puncher who had won 61 of his 80 fights. The winner's purse was £10 and the loser's, £4.

I HOPE YOU GET BASHED.

I AIN'T AS STUPID AS YOU, TUG. I'LL WIN TONIGHT.

I HOPE YOU'VE DONE SOMETHING ABOUT THE SMELL OF GAS, LAZ. IT'S BAD WHEN YOU'RE IN THE RING.

THERE AIN'T NO SMELL OF GAS.

BE CAREFUL WITH THAT CIGAR. I CAN SMELL GAS.

WHAT ABOUT THE SMELL OF GAS IN THE RING?

I CAN'T SMELL GAS. NOW, YOU TWO, I WANT A CLEAN FIGHT.

As the bell signalled the start of the fight, Crib pulled the last part of his bluff.

WATCH THAT MATCH

HE DID WHAT I EXPECTED HIM TO DO.

NINE, TEN, OUT!

COME TO THINK OF IT. I CAN'T SMELL GAS NOW.

YOU'LL LAND IN TROUBLE IF YOU KEEP ON WINNING BY TRICKS. AND YOU DON'T NEED TO—YOU'VE THE MAKING OF A CLASS BOXER.

A pack of cordite charges catches fire—and only Bill Gordon's quick thinking can save H.M.S. Glasgow from blowing up.

GORDON OF THE GLASGOW

I THINK DRESDEN'S GOING TO GET AWAY, SIR. SHE'S FASTER THAN THE OTHER TWO.

SIGNAL KENT TO ATTACK NURNBERG, NUMBER ONE. WE'LL TACKLE THE OTHER TWO.

AYE, AYE, SIR.

ON December 8, 1914, the British light cruiser Glasgow, along with Kent and Cornwall, was chasing three German cruisers in the closing stages of the Battle of the Falkland Islands. On Glasgow's bridge, standing near Captain Luce, was Bridge Messenger Bill Gordon, a young Boy Seaman.

PROBABLY, BUT NOT FOR LONG. LEIPZIG MUST BE THE MAIN TARGET NOW.

WE'LL BE IN ACTION ANY MINUTE NOW.

OPEN FIRE WHEN THE RANGE CLOSES TO 12,000 YARDS!

THAT SHOT FELL WELL ASTERN, SIR. WE JUST HAVEN'T GOT THE HITTING POWER.

WE'VE GOT THE SPEED TO GET CLOSER THOUGH!

LEIPZIG'S GOT THE GUNS ALL RIGHT, SIR. THIS IS GOING TO BE QUITE A FIGHT!

OUR SPEED'S DROPPING. SEE THE ENGINEER COMMANDER, NUMBER ONE, AND GORDON CAN BRING THE REPORT BACK IMMEDIATELY.

AYE, AYE, SIR. COME ON, GORDON!

DO YOU THINK WE'LL CATCH LEIPZIG, SIR?

WE WILL, BOY, EVEN IF WE HAVE TO SHAKE THE SHIP APART!

For over three hours the chase continued, and it was growing dark when—

IF YE WANT MORE SPEED, YE'LL HAVE TO FIND MORE COAL! WE'RE RUNNING LOW AND HAVING TO SHIFT IT FROM THE FURTHEST AWAY BUNKERS.

GORDON, TELL THE CAPTAIN THE POSITION WHILE I CHECK THE BUNKERS.

OH, OH! LEIPZIG'S REALLY OPENING UP NOW!

"We will attack!"

THEY WANT TO CONSERVE THE NEAREST COAL SUPPLIES FOR THE ACTION, SIR.

IF I DON'T GET MORE SPEED, THERE WON'T BE ANY ACTION! CHIEF PETTY OFFICER RILEY—

YES, SIR!

GET WOOD FROM WHEREVER YOU LIKE, BUT FEED THOSE BOILERS. SEND GORDON ROUND TO COLLECT ALL THE SPARE MEN AND ARM THEM WITH AXES. BURN ANYTHING!

AYE, AYE, SIR!

CAN I HAVE A COUPLE OF MEN FOR TEN MINUTES, SIR? THE CAPTAIN WANTS WOOD CUT!

RIGHT, LAD.

START WITH THE CABIN FURNITURE. CHOP UP ANYTHING THAT WILL BURN.

THIS LOT WON'T GO FAR, CHIEF.

ONCE WE'VE STRIPPED THE CABINS WE'LL THINK OF SOMETHING ELSE.

THAT'S THE LOT UP HERE. WE'LL HAVE A GO AT THE DECKS NOW.

HERE'S SOME MORE, LADS.

Aboard Leipzig, the engineer officer reported to Captain Haun.

YOU MUST SLOW DOWN, KAPITAN, OR THE BOILERS WILL BURST.

MAKE WHAT SPEED YOU CAN. THIRTY DEGREES TO PORT. WE WILL ATTACK!

SHE'S SLOWING AND TURNING, CAPTAIN.

35 DEGREES PORT AND SIGNAL CORNWALL TO FOLLOW ME AROUND. INDEPENDENT RAPID FIRE.

GORDON, GET ME A CHECK ON OUR AMMUNITION STOCKS.

90

"Close the range and sink her!"

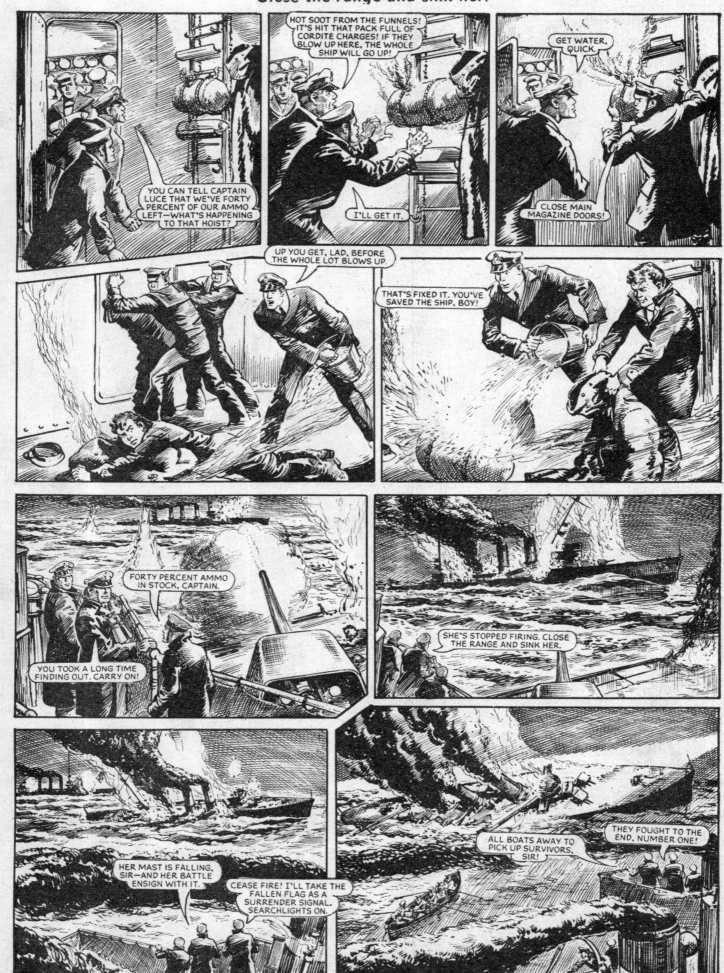

The story of how the Pony Express caught a clever stage-coach robber on the Overland trail.

TALES of the PONY EXPRESS

NA5. STORES & HARDWARE

OVERLAND STAGE LINES

JULESBURG PONY EXPRESS DEPOT

YOU'RE ALL RIGHT, DOC. IN YOU GO.

IS THIS THE WAY YOU WESTERNERS DO BUSINESS? I'VE A TRAIN TO CATCH, AND YOU'VE HELD UP THIS COACH A GOOD TEN MINUTES ASKING SILLY QUESTIONS, MR SLADE.

I'M SORRY TO KEEP YOU GENTLEMEN, BUT I'M DOING A CHECK ON ALL PASSENGERS. THERE ARE TWO HOLD-UP MEN WHO HAVE BEEN OPERATING ON OTHER SECTIONS. ONE PRETENDS HE'S A PASSENGER AND STRIKES FROM INSIDE. I DON'T WANT THAT TO HAPPEN HERE..

Some way along the trail.

Dr. D. GREY MD

OH, OH, THERE GOES THE DOCTOR'S STETHOSCOPE.

YOUR STETHOSCOPE, DOCTOR.

MY WHAT? OH—YES, YES, OF COURSE. THANK YOU SIR, I'LL PUT IT AWAY SAFELY.

DRAT THE THING!

BIT OF A NUISANCE THESE THINGS, AREN'T THEY, DOC?

YES, THEY ARE AWKWARD. I'LL JUST STUFF IT IN MY POCKET UNTIL THE NEXT STOP, THEN I CAN PUT IT PROPERLY IN MY BAG.

TELL ME ONE THING, DOC, AND PUT MY MIND AT REST. MY NEPHEW IS YOUNG AND STRONG, BUT LAST WEEK HE TOOK AN ATTACK OF ECCHYMOSIS. DO YOU THINK HE WILL PULL THROUGH?

WELL, THAT'S A SERIOUS DISEASE, BUT IF HE'S YOUNG AND STRONG, HE SHOULD PULL THROUGH ALL RIGHT.

GEE, THANKS, DOC. THAT SURE IS A RELIEF COMING FROM A MEDICAL MAN LIKE YOURSELF.

YOU'RE WELCOME, SIR.

I DON'T LIKE THE LOOK OF THAT GUY WITH THE EYE PATCH. IF THERE'S A BANDIT IN THIS COACH, IT'LL BE HIM!

The dude with iron in his fists.

Ten minutes later.

HOLD IT, THERE. DROP THEM REINS. THIS IS A HOLD-UP.

SHOTS. IT MUST BE A HOLD-UP! I KNEW I SHOULD NEVER COME OUT WEST.

IT IS INDEED A HOLD-UP, GENTLEMEN, AND IF YOU WILL KINDLY...

Dr. D. GREY

OW!

GOOD WORK, SIR!

LOOK AFTER THAT FAKE DOC, AND I'LL LOOK AFTER THE OTHER HOLD-UP MAN.

HURRY UP THERE, BEN. AIN'T YOU GOT THE PASSENGERS UNDER CONTROL YET?

NO HE AIN'T, BUDDY. NOW DROP THAT GUN!

YOU SHOULD HAVE DROPPED YOUR GUN, BUD. IT WOULD HAVE SAVED YOU A BULLET IN THE ARM.

LOOK AT THE TIME! I'LL MISS MY TRAIN, AND IT'S VITAL I GET TO CONGRESS TO VOTE ON THE GOVERNMENT AID TO TRANSPORT IN THE WEST BILL.

TELL ME, SENATOR, ARE YOU IN FAVOUR OF THE BILL, OR NOT?

IN FAVOUR. IN SPITE OF THE DIFFICULTIES, I THINK THAT WESTERN TRANSPORT FIRMS DO A GRAND JOB.

THEN HOP IN, SENATOR. I'LL DRIVE— AND I'LL MAKE SURE YOU CATCH YOUR TRAIN!

YOU KNOW, JUD, I RECKON I'VE SEEN THIS GUY SOMEWHERE, BUT I'M BLOWED IF I REMEMBER WHERE.

NEVER MIND THAT, RUBE. JUST YOU GET UP THERE, AND WE'LL SEE IF THE DUDE IS AS HANDY WITH THE REINS AS HE IS WITH A GUN.

GIDDUP THERE.

"The crazy fool—he'll kill us all!"

The "dude" soon proved himself a masterly driver. The coach made good time down the mountain trail. But the passengers' adventures were not over for the day. As they turned a sharp bend . . . .

INJUNS!

YOU AIN'T GOING NOWHERE, INDIAN!

GEE UP! IF I KNOW MY INDIANS, THERE WILL BE MORE COMING AFTER US.

YOU'RE RIGHT. HERE THEY COME!

THE INDIANS WILL CATCH US FOR SURE IF WE GO ON DOWN THE TRAIL. THIS IS OUR ONLY CHANCE.

YOU'RE MAD. THE COACH WON'T TAKE IT!,

THE CRAZY FOOL— HE'LL KILL US ALL!

LOOK OUT, BOULDERS!

OKAY, I SEE THEM . . . WHEW, WE'RE DOWN ON THE LEVEL!

ANY SIGN OF THE INDIANS?

NOPE, THAT SHORT CUT OF YOURS LEFT THEM FAR BEHIND— AND THAT'S LINCOLN CITY AHEAD.

WELL, THANK YOU, SIR. THANKS TO YOUR SHORT CUT, I GOT HERE IN TIME. I'VE NEVER SEEN ANYTHING SO FAST—APART FROM THE WAY YOU DEALT WITH THE CROOKED DOCTOR. THAT WAS REAL QUICK THINKING.

NOT REALLY, SENATOR, YOU SEE I WAS WAITING FOR HIM TO MAKE HIS PLAY. I KNEW HE WAS NO DOCTOR. I GOT SUSPICIOUS WHEN I SAW THE AWKWARD WAY HE HANDLED HIS STETHOSCOPE. THESE SUSPICIONS WERE CONFIRMED WHEN I ASKED HIM ABOUT ECCHYMOSIS.

THAT'S WHAT I GOT LAST WEEK, ACCORDING TO MY DOCTOR, WHEN A COACH DOOR FLEW OPEN AND HIT ME. ECCHYMOSIS, YOU SEE . . .

. . . IS A BLACK EYE!

WELL, THAT WAS REAL SMART OF YOU, SIR.

NOW I KNOW HIM.

HIS PICTURE IS HUNG UP IN THE PONY EXPRESS OFFICE— THAT'S WILLIAM RUSSEL OF RUSSEL, WADDELL AND MAJORS' TRANSPORT COMPANY—AND BOSS OF THE PONY EXPRESS!

AND TO THINK I HAD HIM FIGURED FOR JUST ANOTHER WESTERN DUDE!

The Pony Express made men tough. ON PAGE 142 you'll find what it did for "Maverick" Carson

Attacked by hordes of deadly vampire bats, the lockmaster is in one of the tightest spots of his career!

THE NAME IS LOCKE

SAM LOCKE sat up in bed, startled into wakefulness by the deep, sonorous notes of a striking clock.

The sound carried across the valley to the little Austrian mountain village where he had his lodgings.

"Midnight!" he muttered, and found himself counting the strokes. ". . . nine, ten, eleven, twelve——" There was another clang, and another. "Hey, what's this? It can't strike fourteen!"

But it did. Not only did the distant clock strike fourteen, but it went on to fifteen, sixteen, seventeen, and still further.

"What's the matter with the blasted thing?" he muttered, slipping from the bed and going to the open casement window.

He looked across the valley in the direction of the striking clock. The sound came from what appeared to be an old castle on the mountainside, about a mile away.

A footfall below the window made him look down. It was the elderly village policeman.

"Isn't anyone going to stop that clock?" asked Locke, loudly.

The man looked up.

"It will stop in its own good time, Herr Locke," he replied, for in that small village everyone knew the lockmaster. Everyone knew he was there to see and value the collection of locks left by Old Bruck, a former watchmaker who had recently died.

"It will sound until the moon sets."

"What has the moon got to do with it?" asked Locke.

"We do not know," the old policeman told him. "But it always stops when the moon sets."

"Whose clock is it? Why doesn't the owner have it seen to?"

"The clock is in the old castle and no one lives there now," murmured the Austrian. "Nobody will stay there since what happened to Graf Vorder. Nobody will go near the place after dark."

"Why won't anyone go there?" the lockmaster asked.

"Because of the vampires, Herr Locke,"

the policeman replied. "They killed Graf Vorder and all his family, and they now start the clock striking about twice a month."

"Surely you don't believe in such things, Sergeant?" scoffed Locke.

"I do, Herr Locke, and so does everyone else in the valley," affirmed the policeman. "Even if the tower was not secured by a lock that none can open, no one would go there and try to stop the clock."

The lockmaster pricked up his ears. Locks were to him the most fascinating things in the world. He was probably the greatest living expert on them. He had designed many of the locks and strongrooms of the Carson Safe Company, which employed him to travel widely in search of unusual locks, and to find out whether anything could be learned from them.

The suggestion that a lock could not be mastered was a challenge which he never refused.

"I shall never be able to sleep with that noise going on, so I might as well go across there and stop the clock myself," he announced.

"Herr Locke! Herr Locke!" came the agitated voice of the police sergeant through the window. "I beg of you not to do that. It is dangerous. In any case, you cannot enter the tower. The door at the top is locked. Many have tried to open it—in daylight—but all have failed."

"Locks are my job," replied Locke, as he slid into his trousers.

Five minutes later, he emerged by the side door of the inn, and found Sergeant Gussing awaiting him. The old man was genuinely scared.

"Herr Locke, I beg you not to go there. Something will happen to you!" he insisted.

"Nonsense! What can happen to me? I don't believe in your vampire bats, and I've yet to find the lock that I can't master," Locke told him. "Be a good chap and show me the shortest way to the castle."

Unwillingly, the police sergeant showed him the way across the valley. By this time there were many lights in the houses in the village, and they could hear people talking, but nobody showed themselves at the windows, which were all tightly closed.

Soon they were on the farther side of the valley, away from the village, and Locke could see that the castle was surrounded by tall, gloomy pine trees. There was a belt of these on the lower part of the slope, and at the edge of it Sergeant Gussing stopped abruptly.

"I dare not come any farther, Herr Locke!" he exclaimed.

"Don't make such a fuss about it," chuckled Locke. "Wait here for me if you like. Unless I'm mistaken about that lock, I'll have stopped the clock and will be back here in half an hour."

INTO THE CASTLE.

THE police sergeant shrugged helplessly as Locke stepped between the trees and was almost at once in total darkness. The branches of the pines met overhead.

But he had come prepared for this, and now switched on his powerful torch. By its aid he was able to follow the path upwards.

Finally he emerged from the pines and stood in front of the castle.

The clock was at the top of the tower at the left end of the building. It was about eighty feet from the ground.

There was a door at the foot of the tower, and the lockmaster strode over to this.

The lockmaster had brought a tool kit in his pocket, and he had the door open within a minute. Inside was a circular room, quite bare, with a stone-flagged floor. A steep flight of steps wound its way to the upper part of the tower.

At the top of the steps there was another massive door. Evidently this cut off the room in which the mechanism and striking gear of the clock were installed. From behind that door came the whirring of cogs and the steady clang-clang-clang of the hammer on the bell.

He went up another step and shone his torch on the lock.

A low whistle escaped his lips. Sergeant Gussing had been right. This was no ordinary lock. It was of a design made famous by an Italian locksmith named Garguilo, and Locke had only seen one like it before.

"Aha!" he muttered. "I shall have to be on my mettle to master this beauty."

Even as he said this, there came from below the solid thud of a closing door. It sounded like the main door of the tower. Locke turned his torch downwards and went racing down the steps at a reckless pace.

The main door was fast closed!

He went over and tugged at it, but it was locked. He stood there frowning at this massive barrier. He knew it had not closed accidentally. No sudden gust of wind had done this, for he had wedged it open.

He could not operate the lock from the inside because there was no keyhole there. The mechanism of the lock was entirely on the other side and in the thickness of the door.

He turned away from the closed door. There was only one other way of exit. He must go through the clock-room on to the roof of the tower.

this he held his torch with the other hand, shining it straight ahead as he pushed the door inwards.

THE BATTLE WITH THE BATS.

THEN came a rush of movement as scores of small bodies hurtled through the air and hit him on the head, face and body.

The torch was knocked from his startled grasp, and went bouncing down the stone steps. The light went out. The jolt had broken the bulb.

The lockmaster found himself on the darkened steps, lashing out wildly at the things which

But first he would have to defeat that Italian lock at the top of the stairs !

Confronted by the locked door at the top of the steps, Locke wedged his torch so that it gave him some light on the subject, and unrolled his tool kit.

It was a kit which any cracksman would have given much to have possessed. Now he selected something not unlike a surgeon's probe, and delicately began to explore the inside of the lock.

After a minute or so he picked up a magnetised tool with which he hoped to move some of the interior bolts of the lock. Very carefully he began to slide one of these bolts along.

He felt another bolt moving. Good progress was being made. There were four interior bolts, and he had already moved over two of them. He calculated that in another half-hour he would have the door open.

The third bolt was mastered. His back was aching through bending.

He attached his magnet to the fourth bolt. It was a little stiffer than the others, but he felt a slight movement in the right direction.

At last ! He detached the magnet, eased the tool out of the lock and turned the heavy iron ring handle. As he did

clung to his hair and face.

They were bats, hundreds of them.

As he struggled to maintain his balance, something bit deeply into the back of his hand. Something else pricked the back of his neck.

Then he knew that these were vampire bats and he would have to fight for his life.

Wanting more room in which to battle with his unseen and sinister opponents, the lockmaster plunged across the threshold into the clock-room.

Sufficient light came in through the slits on all four sides of the tower to show him the big cogwheels and gearing of the clock.

As he beat at the air before him to keep the bats from his face, Locke stumbled over something and fell across it. It felt like a crate of some description, and as he scrambled to one side he found himself in contact with another.

There was not much room to fight the bats in the clock-room, for it appeared to be used as a storehouse for crates, barrels, and bales.

The bats swept back to the attack. As fast as he knocked one aside, another hurled itself against him.

Then in one corner he saw an empty sack, snatched it up,

and waved it wildly around his head. Many bats were smashed or disabled. Most of the others fled out through the door or by way of the openings. Locke had time to strike a match and look around.

Just as he had expected, there was a trap-door leading to the open roof.

Then he remembered why he had come there, struck another match, and bent over the clock. There was no time to find the correct way of stopping the striker. Instead, he grasped the little hammer between his fingers and bent the arm over to one side, so that it no longer made contact with the bell.

Waving the sack wildly, he drove away the last of the bats, then closed the door leading to the staircase.

He climbed to the top of the clock and reached for the trap-door.

It was very stiff on its hinges. It felt as though it had not been raised for many years, but with an effort he sent it crashing back and moonlight poured in.

The lockmaster looked again at the various stacks of crates, boxes, and bundles. Many of them had markings on them in the Slav language.

Locke began to understand. "Smugglers!" he murmured. "So that's the explanation ! The frontier with Yugoslavia is only a mile or so away. Smugglers have been using this supposedly haunted castle as a store."

That explained many things, but the only explanation of the closing of the lower door was that one of the smugglers must be outside. It was not a pleasant thought.

The lockmaster gripped the edge of the opening above him and hauled himself up. When he had got his head and shoulders over the edge, he was able to crawl out on to the roof of the tower.

Clouds were sweeping over the moon. He could not see beyond the enclosing belts of pines. He lay on his face and peered over the edge of the roof in the direction of the door by which he had entered.

Nobody was in sight. It was possible that after shutting him in the tower the lone member of the gang had hurried off to warn his comrades of the intruder.

"The question is, will they be coming back ?" Sam pondered. "Now that the clock has stopped they'll know I've entered the clock-room. Probably they set it striking as a signal to those across the frontier, and because they know that the mystery of the striking clock frightens everyone in the valley. I'd better be out of here before they return."

It was about 80 feet to the ground below, and the rough stone blocks of which the tower was made offered no handhold.

Then he remembered that many of the bundles and boxes in the clock-room were roped. He lowered himself inside again, and set to work to untie and collect all these pieces of rope.

When he had collected all the pieces of rope, he tied them together and looked at the resulting length. Would it be long enough for his purpose? Would it be strong enough to take his weight?

There was nothing on the roof to which he could attach one end of the rope, so he had to waste some of the valuable length by bringing it inside and fastening it to the upper framework of the clock. He tested the rope as best he could by tugging on it with all his strength. None of the knots slipped, but that did not prove that the rope would not break.

Back again to the top of the tower, and he lowered the rope over the side. It went within about sixteen feet of the ground, but no further.

He swung over the side, and very gingerly began to descend hand over hand, bracing his feet against the wall to try to take off some of the strain.

However, the moment came when his groping right hand found no more rope. He looked down, and the ground seemed dangerously far away, but he lowered himself as far as possible, until he was hanging at arm's length below the rope, bent his knees slightly, and dropped.

THE SMUGGLERS.

HE landed with a jarring thud and rolled over. Apart from a few bruises, there was no damage done. As he picked himself up, there was a sudden rush of feet from under the trees, and he found himself confronted by five tough-looking characters, all armed with cudgels.

He recognised one of the village men, but the others were strangers to him.

"Interfering foreign dog!" snarled one, and struck at Locke with his club.

The lockmaster dodged the blow, ducked his head, and rammed his assailant in the stomach.

The smuggler had not been expecting that, and went over backwards, whereupon Locke was off like a hare for the edge of the woods.

It was too dark under the trees to see anything, but he made sure he was running downhill, and as he ran he bellowed at the top of his voice—

"Sergeant Gussing! Sergeant Gussing!"

Many times he collided with trees, and by the time he emerged on the lower slope he was bruised, torn, and blood-stained. But a uniformed figure was moving towards him. Sergeant Gussing had awaited his return.

At sight of Locke in that sorry plight, the Austrian paled.

"Are they after you, Herr Locke?" he gasped. "Was it the vampire bats? Let us get away from here while we can! We must run!"

He grabbed the lockmaster's arm and tried to drag him away. Locke had been too breathless to speak, but now he blurted out—

"It's not the bats that are

after me but smugglers! They've been using the castle as a headquarters."

Sergeant Gussing stopped, and unbuttoned the flap of his holster. No longer was he afraid. Vampire bats were something he would not face, but smugglers were a different matter.

"Where are the scoundrels?" he demanded, and at that moment three of them burst out of the woods.

They paused at sight of the grey-moustached sergeant, then turned to run back, but a shot over their heads and his stern order to stop brought them up sharply with their hands over their heads.

Locke helped the sergeant secure them and march them back to the village. The other two members of the gang escaped across the frontier, but they were obliged to leave behind all the goods stored in the clock-room of the tower. It was a rich haul, and earned the sergeant a substantial reward, but by the time he got that Locke was far away from Austria, pursuing his interst in locks, elsewhere.

**NEXT STORY
ON PAGE 150**

Braddock leads the way in a daring low-level raid deep into Germany—and the fighters are waiting!

I FLEW WITH BRADDOCK

Sergeant Matt Braddock, V.C., was the greatest pilot of the last war. This is the story of the famous book about him, written by George Bourne, his navigator. Braddock was to make a special mission to drop a big, new bomb designed by Mr Smith, a brilliant scientist. Mr Smith pulled strings, and a signal was sent from Group Headquarters, grounding Braddock and his crew till the special raid. But Group Captain Mandeville, the commanding officer at Barminster aerodrome, ignored the signal, hoping that he would be allowed to drop the big bomb if Braddock failed to return from a raid. Now F Fox, Braddock's plane, was taking part in an attack on a vital target in Germany.

NAVIGATOR TO PILOT. ENEMY COAST AHEAD. TURNING POINT IN TEN MINUTES. NEW COURSE WILL BE 080 DEGREES TRUE.

The Lancasters zig-zagged at zero feet towards their target in Germany.

REAR GUNNER TO SKIPPER—FIGHTERS SEVEN O'CLOCK HIGH. HERE THEY COME.

GOT IT! GOT IT!

GOOD SHOOTING, LAD!

NAVIGATOR TO PILOT. VABRUK TWELVE MINUTES AHEAD.

OKAY, GEORGE, WE'LL GO IN LOW.

FIGHTER ON OUR TAIL, SKIPPER. WE'RE BEING HIT!

MID-UPPER GUNNER HERE, SKIPPER. I'VE SWATTED THAT FIGHTER.

Distress flares from F Fox.

GOOD SHOW, ARTHUR. YOU'VE SAVED OUR BACON. BOMB DOORS OPEN. TARGET AHEAD. TAKE OVER, BOMB AIMER!

LEFT, LEFT—STEADY—BOMBS GONE!

BANG ON THE TARGET!

REAR GUNNER HERE, SKIPPER. OUR TAILPLANE IS SCUPPERED.

WIRELESS OPERATOR HERE, SKIPPER. THE WIRELESS HAS GONE.

HAM HERE, BRAD. THE PORT OUTER ENGINE IS PACKING UP.

THAT'S A RIGHT TALE OF WOE YOU LOT HAVE GIVEN ME. BUT NEVER MIND, WE'RE STILL FLYING. GIVE ME A ZIG ZAG COURSE FOR HOME, GEORGE. IT WILL FOOL THE FIGHTERS!

The damaged Lanc limped towards home. All went well until it was crossing the French coast.

IT'S AN ACK-ACK SHIP. DIVE, BRAD, DIVE!

WHEW, THAT WAS A HOT FOUR MINUTES, BRAD. GLAD YOU MANAGED TO GET AWAY SO QUICKLY.

YES, IT WAS ROTTEN LUCK TO FLY OVER AN ANTI-AIRCRAFT SHIP. IT NEARLY GOT US, TOO. A SHELL SEVERED THE RUDDER CABLES.

WE SHOULD BE NEAR THE FIGHTER DROME AT MAVINGTON NOW, BRAD. I'LL PUSH OUT SOME DISTRESS FLARES!

THERE IT IS, BRAD, THEY'VE SWITCHED ON THE ILLUMINATIONS FOR US.

F Fox landed safely, but knocked down some telephone wires—which meant an uncomfortable time for Mandeville, back at Barminster.

" I'm sorry to say Braddock's plane was shot down in flames!"

I WARN YOU, MANDEVILLE, IF ANYTHING HAPPENS TO MR BRADDOCK, YOU'RE FOR IT.

HERE COME THE FIRST OF THE LANCS NOW, MR SMITH. WE'LL SOON HAVE NEWS OF YOUR PRECIOUS BRADDOCK.

WELL, HOWERTH. HOW DID IT GO? WAS IT A GOOD SHOW?

GRIM, WE HAD TO FIGHT OUR WAY IN AND OUT AGAIN. WE LOST A LOT OF CHAPS.

NEVER MIND ALL THAT. HOW ABOUT MR BRADDOCK?

I'M AFRAID HIS PLANE WAS SHOT DOWN IN FLAMES!

Mandeville's career seemed in ruins. He tried to shift the blame to someone else, but failed. Mr Smith phoned Air Vice-Marshal Pringell, who came racing to Barminster in his car.

THAT FOOL SENT MR BRADDOCK ON AN ORDINARY RAID, WHEN HE HAD BEEN ORDERED TO SUSPEND HIM FROM FLYING UNTIL HE WAS READY TO DROP MY BOMB.

BUT I KNEW NOTHING OF THE SIGNAL. IT COULDN'T HAVE GOT TO ME. PROBABLY IT WAS MISLAID IN THE ADJUTANT'S OFFICE.

I BEG YOUR PARDON, SIR, BUT I PERSONALLY BROUGHT THE SIGNAL TO YOUR NOTICE!

A PHONE CALL FOR AIR VICE MARSHAL PRINGELL. PLEASE.

THIS IS SERIOUS, MANDEVILLE. THE MATTER WILL HAVE TO BE FULLY INVESTIGATED.

A few minutes later.

BRADDOCK IS SAFE. HOWERTH EVIDENTLY CONFUSED F FOX WITH ANOTHER VICTIM. BUT BRADDOCK HAS A NASTY FLESH WOUND IN HIS SHOULDER, CAUSED BY A FRAGMENT OF ACK-ACK SHELL.

NOBODY IS MORE RELIEVED THAN 'I. IF THROUGH PRESSURE OF WORK, I OVERLOOKED THE SIGNAL, AND I'VE NO RECOLLECTION OF EVER SEEING IT, I REGRET THE OCCURENCE AND AM THANKFUL THAT BRADDOCK RETURNED.

Braddock's wound did not keep him out of action for long. Soon he was supervising repairs to F Fox. The plane was also modified to carry the big bomb. A few days later, the bomb arrived at the station, and Brad was called to a briefing with two naval officers.

HERE IS THE TARGET FOR YOUR BIG BOMB, BRADDOCK. IT'S THE GERMANS' LATEST AIRCRAFT CARRIER, THE DEGEN. THAT MEANS THE "SWORD", I BELIEVE, AND IT WOULD CUT A SWATHE THROUGH OUR ATLANTIC CONVOYS IF IT ESCAPED IN THE MISTS FROM KIEL.

KIEL'S A TOUGH TARGET. WE'LL NEED PATHFINDERS TO LIGHT THE PLACE UP FOR US. WHAT'S THE WEATHER FORECAST?

PATHFINDER SQUADRONS ARE GOING ON AHEAD OF YOU. THE FORECAST IS GOOD. THERE WILL BE NO MORE THAN LIGHT CLOUD.

THEN WE SHALL GO IN AT 6000 FEET. FROM THAT HEIGHT, USING THE NEW BOMBSIGHT, WE SHOULD BE ON TARGET.

BUT THAT'S SUICIDE, MAN. KIEL IS ONE OF THE MOST HEAVILY DEFENDED TARGETS IN THE WORLD. AT 6000 FEET, THE DEFENCES WILL MURDER YOU!

TO HIT THE SHIP FROM A HIGHER ALTITUDE WOULD NEED A LOT OF LUCK. WE'VE GOT TO TAKE A CHANCE TO MAKE SURE OF DESTROYING THE DEGEN.

CONTINUED ON PAGE 130 Mandeville has Braddock right where he wants him —— in a prison cell!

Never has the Rovers' ground held so many spectators. It is packed to capacity, yet the manager is moaning—not a penny has been taken at the turnstiles!

GORGEOUS GUS

OH CRUMBS, HERE HE COMES AGAIN. WHY DIDN'T I TAKE UP A NICE COMFY JOB LIKE WRESTLING CROCODILES?

The Earl of Boote bought Redburn Rovers, a First Division football club, and played centre-forward for them. The earl was at once nicknamed Gorgeous Gus by the fans, because of his immaculate appearance and the numerous flunkeys who attended him—He refused to run for the ball. He demanded perfect passes, and when he got them, he proved to have the hardest shot ever seen in soccer! Now Rovers were playing Granton Villa, and were winning 1-0, Gus having scored with a blockbuster. Then he got another shooting chance.

BOY, AM I GLAD I WASN'T IN FRONT OF THAT ONE!

GOAL! WHAT A SHOT! BUT HEY, LOOK. GUS IS WALKING OFF.

YES, HE ALWAYS WALKS OFF AFTER HE'S SCORED TWO GOALS, HE RECKONS HE'S DONE ENOUGH.

Later, Rovers were leading by two goals to nil, with only seconds to go, when Gorgeous Gus sneaked out of the players' entrance to his little car—but found the road blocked.

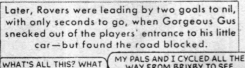

WHAT'S ALL THIS? WHAT HAS HAPPENED? WHY ARE YOU CRYING, BOY?

MY PALS AND I CYCLED ALL THE WAY FROM BRIXBY TO SEE GORGEOUS GUS. BUT THE MEN ELBOWED US OUT OF THE WAY AND THE GATES WERE CLOSED BEFORE WE COULD GET IN!

IT'S THE SAME EVERY WEEK, MISTER.

HEY, LOOK, LADS! IT'S GORGEOUS GUS HIMSELF!

GORGEOUS GUS!

YOU WILL ALL STAND PERFECTLY STILL. I HAVE SOMETHING TO SAY TO YOU.

THANK YOU FOR YOUR INTEREST IN MYSELF, AND I REGRET YOU WERE UNABLE TO SEE TODAY'S GAME. NEXT WEEK WILL BE DIFFERENT FOR THE MATCH AGAINST BILSTON. THE TURNSTILES WILL BE OPEN EARLY AND EVERYONE UNDER FIFTEEN WILL BE ADMITTED FREE. NO ADULTS WILL BE ALLOWED IN THE GROUND UNTIL AFTER TWO O'CLOCK. BE HERE BEFORE TWO AND YOU'LL BE SURE OF SEEING THE MATCH.

GOOD OLD GORGEOUS GUS!

Next Saturday, from all over Redburn, and the district for miles around, boys marched on the Rovers' ground, intent on seeing Gorgeous Gus—and a free football match! Of course, there were some attempts by adults to get in free, too . . . .

COME ON, GRANDPA, IT'S FIFTEEN AND UNDER WHO GET IN AT THIS TIME, AND IT MUST BE FIFTY YEARS SINCE YOU WERE FIFTEEN.

I JUST WANTED TO SEE THE MATCH, MATE, WITH ALL THESE BLOOMING KIDS COMING, THERE WON'T BE ROOM FOR US BY TWO O'CLOCK!

The shot that silenced a soccer loud-mouth.

The old-timer was right. By two o'clock, the ground was packed full of boys.

HAVE YOU EVER HEARD SUCH A DIN, AND EVER SEEN SUCH A SIGHT? THE GROUND IS PACKED TO CAPACITY AND WE HAVEN'T TAKEN A HALFPENNY AT THE TURNSTILES!

COME ON THE ROVERS! GOOD OLD GORGEOUS GUS!

COO, LOOK AT THAT, BERT. HE MUST BE A BIG CISSY WITH ALL THESE SERVANTS AN' ALL!

PAY NO ATTENTION TO THAT, CHUM. THAT'S JUST HIS WAY. GORGEOUS GUS IS NO CISSY. WAIT TILL YOU SEE HIM SHOOT.

THAT'S QUARTER OF AN HOUR GONE AND GUS HASN'T TOUCHED THE BALL YET, BERT.

DO SOMETHING, GORGEOUS GUS, YOU LONG STREAK OF MISERY! DO YOU THINK YOU'VE TAKEN ROOT?

LEAVE GORGEOUS GUS ALONE. HE'S A GREAT PLAYER—OUCH!

SCRAM, YOU KIDS! LEAVE ME ALONE WHILE I TELL THAT FANCY CLOWN WHAT I THINK OF HIM.

HAW! HAW! HAW! SOMEBODY'S GIVEN GORGEOUS GUS THE BALL AT LAST! HE'S NOT A STATUE AFTER ALL. LOOK, HE'S ACTUALLY MOVING.

HE'S MISSED! I'VE NEVER SEEN HIM MISS FROM THAT RANGE BEFORE.

But Gus had not missed!

I APOLOGISE FOR NOT SCORING, MY MAN, BUT THAT FELLOW HAD TO BE DEALT WITH. HE HAD NO BUSINESS TO BE HERE. I DON'T LIKE SENSELESS BARRACKING, AND WORST OF ALL, HE STARTED CHASTISING THE CHILDREN. HE HAD TO GO THEN—BUT I DIDN'T HIT THE BALL TOO HARD!

GOSH, THEN YOU MEANT IT! I THOUGHT YOU HAD MISSED!

Then Jenkins, the butler, who was playing outside-left for the Rovers, got the ball.

LOOK AT THAT BUTLER GO! HEY, GIVE IT TO GUS NOW. YOUR BOSS IS IN THE CLEAR.

TO YOU, SIR. I HOPE IT IS TO YOUR LIKING.

ADMIRABLE, JENKINS. JUST THE WAY I LIKE IT.

" Do you think I'm frightened by a mere mob?"

CONTINUED ON PAGE 134 El Gato, the Cat, is the world's best goalkeeper —— but he's never faced a shot like Gus's!

The hunters' supply of food grows short—and Morgyn makes sure it stays that way!

SEVEN TRAILS TO MORGYN THE MIGHTY

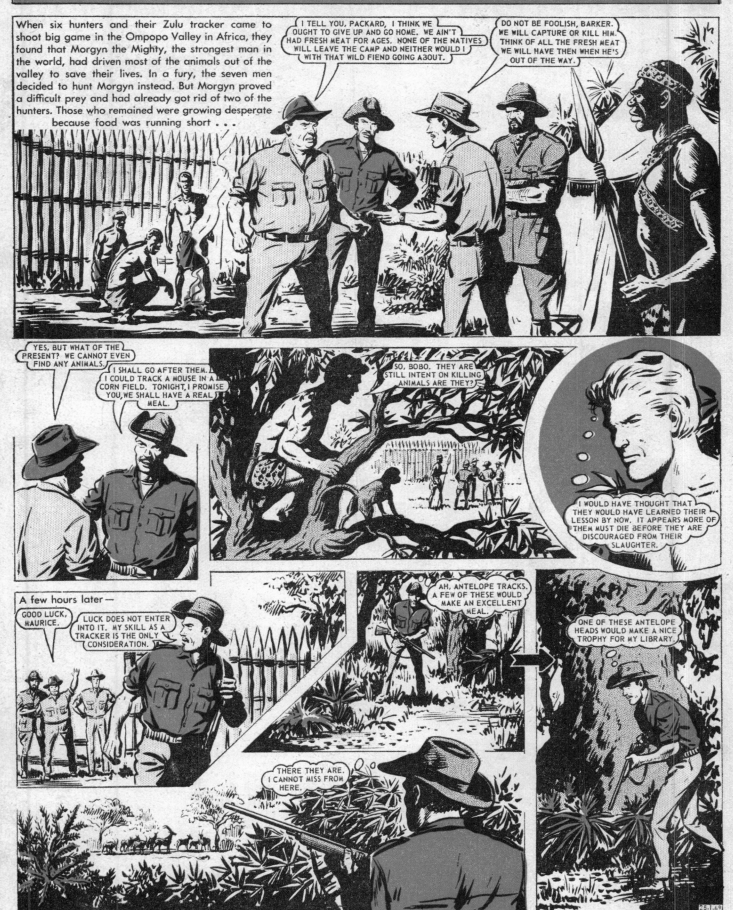

When six hunters and their Zulu tracker came to shoot big game in the Ompopo Valley in Africa, they found that Morgyn the Mighty, the strongest man in the world, had driven most of the animals out of the valley to save their lives. In a fury, the seven men decided to hunt Morgyn instead. But Morgyn proved a difficult prey and had already got rid of two of the hunters. Those who remained were growing desperate because food was running short . . .

I TELL YOU, PACKARD, I THINK WE OUGHT TO GIVE UP AND GO HOME. WE AIN'T HAD FRESH MEAT FOR AGES. NONE OF THE NATIVES WILL LEAVE THE CAMP AND NEITHER WOULD I WITH THAT WILD FIEND GOING ABOUT.

DO NOT BE FOOLISH, BARKER. WE WILL CAPTURE OR KILL HIM. THINK OF ALL THE FRESH MEAT WE WILL HAVE THEN WHEN HE'S OUT OF THE WAY.

YES, BUT WHAT OF THE PRESENT? WE CANNOT EVEN FIND ANY ANIMALS.

I SHALL GO AFTER THEM. I COULD TRACK A MOUSE IN A CORN FIELD. TONIGHT, I PROMISE YOU, WE SHALL HAVE A REAL MEAL.

SO, BOBO. THEY ARE STILL INTENT ON KILLING ANIMALS ARE THEY?

I WOULD HAVE THOUGHT THAT THEY WOULD HAVE LEARNED THEIR LESSON BY NOW. IT APPEARS MORE OF THEM MUST DIE BEFORE THEY ARE DISCOURAGED FROM THEIR SLAUGHTER.

A few hours later —

GOOD LUCK, MAURICE.

LUCK DOES NOT ENTER INTO IT. MY SKILL AS A TRACKER IS THE ONLY CONSIDERATION.

AH, ANTELOPE TRACKS. A FEW OF THESE WOULD MAKE AN EXCELLENT MEAL.

ONE OF THESE ANTELOPE HEADS WOULD MAKE A NICE TROPHY FOR MY LIBRARY.

THERE THEY ARE. I CANNOT MISS FROM HERE.

"Now you shall die."

The hunters use a new weapon against Morgyn ON PAGE 136 — poisoned meat!

THE TOUGH of the TRACK

Alf changes his address — and misses an important letter.

" Be at the flying field at eight sharp tomorrow morning."

ONE OR TWO, ALF. I'M TAKING A PLANE ON A TRIAL FLIGHT TO ANTWERP ON SATURDAY MORNING. WELL, WE'D BETTER PUSH OFF. WE'VE A CONFERENCE TO ATTEND.

SEE YOU AGAIN, THEN.

On Friday evening Alf was in Sam Kessick's cafe.

I SEE YOU'VE MOVED INTO THE OLD BARGE ALF. HOW ARE YOU GETTING ON THERE?

NOT BAD, SAM. THERE ARE ONE OR TWO LEAKY PLANKS IN THE DECK, BUT I'LL SOON GET THEM PLUGGED UP.

HEY, ALF, I DIDN'T KNOW YOU'D MOVED FROM THE VIADUCT. I PUT A LETTER FOR YOU UNDER THE DOOR A FEW DAYS AGO.

COO, I'D BETTER GO AND GET IT, THEN.

Half an hour later, at the viaduct.

AH, THERE IT IS. I'LL GET IT OUT WITH A STICK.

GOT IT.

BLIMEY, AN INVITATION TO THE EUROPEAN GAMES! AND THEY'RE TOMORROW! THE TEAM'S ALREADY LEFT FOR BRUSSELS—JUST MY LUCK! WAIT A MINUTE, THOUGH—ANTWERP'S IN BELGIUM, TOO. I'LL PHONE JOHN GRESHAM.

...AND SO IF YOU COULD GIVE ME A LIFT TO ANTWERP, I COULD HITCH TO BRUSSELS IN TIME.

I SHOULD BE ABLE TO FIX THAT, ALF. BE AT THE FLYING FIELD AT EIGHT SHARP TOMORROW MORNING.

Next morning, Alf travelled to Antwerp in the plane Gresham was testing, and soon he was trying to hitch a lift on the main road to Brussels.

GOOD, HE'S SLOWING DOWN.

BONJOUR, MONSIEUR. ALLEZ-VOUS—

NEVER MIND THAT STUFF, LAD. I'M FROM LANCASHIRE. IF YOU'RE GOING TO BRUSSELS, HOP IN.

THANKS, MISTER. I'M GLAD I DIDN'T HAVE TO EXPLAIN MYSELF IN FRENCH.

AYE, WITH YOUR ACCENT YOU MIGHT HAVE ENDED UP IN MADRID!

Later, outside the Hotel Splendide in Brussels.

CHEERIO, MATE, AND THANKS.

IT'S TUPPER! HOW DID HE GET HERE?

HE DIDN'T REPLY TO THE LETTER I SENT HIM. HIS PLACE HAS BEEN FILLED NOW. PETER WHITTINGTON IS RUNNING IN THE 1500 METRES.

" Fancy coming all this way just to watch!"

I'M SORRY, TUPPER, BUT YOU'LL HAVE TO BE CONTENT TO BE RESERVE. YOU SHOULD HAVE REPLIED TO YOUR INVITATION.

I DIDN'T GET IT TILL YESTERDAY. I CHANGED ME ADDRESS.

That afternoon, on the British team's bus on the way to the stadium.

COO, FANCY COMING ALL THIS WAY JUST TO WATCH!

HEY, WHAT DOES THAT SAY?

IT IS AN ANNOUNCEMENT OF A SPORTS MEETING IN THE FOOTBALL GROUND THIS AFTERNOON. IT IS ONLY A SMALL AFFAIR.

STOP THE BUS. I WANT TO GET OFF.

WHERE ARE YOU GOING, TUPPER?

I'M GOING IN THERE. I AIN'T STANDING ABOUT ALL AFTERNOON WHEN I CAN HAVE A RUN. SEE YOU LATER.

I'LL HAVE TO FIND SOMEONE WHO SPEAKS ENGLISH.

Luckily, the sports organiser spoke English.

WE ARE DELIGHTED TO HAVE YOU, MONSIEUR TUPPAIRE. ENTER FOR ANY EVENTS YOU LIKE. THE FIRST RACE IS A 2000 METRES HANDICAP EVENT. WOULD YOU LIKE TO GO IN FOR THAT?

GOOD. THIS WILL GIVE OUR SPORTS AN INTERNATIONAL FLAVOUR. COME, I WILL SHOW YOU WHERE TO CHANGE.

YES, I WOULD. I'LL PLAY FAIR WITH YOU. I'VE HAD A LOT OF PRACTICE AT RUNNING, AND I'LL BE SATISFIED TO START FROM SCRATCH.

When the 2000 metres was due to start, Alf found he was the only scratch man.

COO, I'VE GOT A LOT OF GROUND TO MAKE UP.

THAT LOT DIDN'T TAKE MUCH PASSING...

"It's now or never."

CONTINUED ON PAGE 138 Alf wins a gold medal — and a cuckoo clock!

Dennison has to fire the most difficult shot of his career — he has to kill a friend

110

"The plan has misfired!"

The two men negotiated the cliff and were on the tower when Dupont lost his footing and dropped the bag of detonators into the sea.

OKAY, DUPONT. I'VE GOT YOU. FEEL FOR ANOTHER FOOTHOLD!

MADE IT!

IN DAYLIGHT YOU CAN LOOK DOWN INTO THE ROOM WHERE THE TRAITOR DOES HIS FOUL WORK. THEN YOU MUST SHOOT HIM, DENNISON!

THE PLAN HAS MISFIRED, DUPONT. THE GERMANS HAVE ARMOUR-PLATED SHUTTERS FITTED TO THE WINDOW!

THE TRAITOR SHALL NOT ESCAPE JUSTICE! I HAVE ANOTHER PLAN. LISTEN AND I WILL TELL IT TO YOU—!

Dupont quickly explained his plan.

I CANNOT DO AS YOU SUGGEST, DUPONT!

I BEG YOU TO. WE HAVE EXPLOSIVES BUT NO DETONATORS. IT IS THE ONLY WAY TO STOP PIERRE AND HIS VILE EXPERIMENTS. AS I TOLD YOU, IT IS A MATTER OF FAMILY HONOUR.

With a heavy heart, Dennison sighted his rifle on the pack of explosives and fired.

Seconds later, Marcel Dupont surrendered to the Germans.

MARCEL HAS ASKED ME TO FIRE THE MOST DIFFICULT SHOT OF MY LIFE. FOR HIS SAKE I MUST DO IT!

SHOOT NOW, DENNISON! SHOOT STRAIGHT! HELP ME TO WIPE OUT THE STAIN ON THE NAME OF DUPONT.

STRANGE HOW TWO BROTHERS COULD BE SO DIFFERENT. PIERRE DUPONT, SCIENTIST AND TRAITOR! MARCEL DUPONT WHO PUT FAMILY HONOUR BEFORE EVERYTHING!

GOODBYE, MARCEL. YOU WERE THE WORST CAR DRIVER I EVER MET—AND THE BRAVEST MAN! I AM PROUD TO HAVE KNOWN YOU!

Five thousand pounds to save "The Clarion's" face! That is the price the paper must pay—or Joe Doone doesn't play for England!

IS IT CRICKET?

The Australians' 1961 Tour of England had started off with a resounding victory in the First Test. But Ted Stevens, sports reporter of the Daily Clarion, had brought hope to England's selectors. In the wilds of the West Country he had discovered Joe Doone, a 18-year-old bowling wizard—who had never played cricket in his life! The Clarion had persuaded the selectors to pick Joe for the Second Test. Now disaster had struck, for Brandon Marsh, a scheming reporter, had kidnapped Joe and was holding him to ransom.

SO THAT'S HOW IT IS, GENTS! I WANT FIVE THOUSAND POUNDS—OR JOE DOESN'T PLAY FOR ENGLAND TOMORROW. THAT WILL MAKE THE CLARION LOOK REALLY SILLY!

YOU'LL GET YOUR MONEY, MARSH. BUT SOME DAY I'LL MAKE YOU PAY FOR THIS!

YOU HAD BETTER HAVE THE MONEY READY BY TWO O'CLOCK. I'LL BE BACK FOR IT THEN!

AND DON'T CALL THE POLICE. THEY COULDN'T FIND DOONE WHERE I HAVE HIM HIDDEN!

TAKE EVERY AVAILABLE MAN IN THE OFFICE, STEVENS, AND FIND JOE DOONE! I WANT HIM HERE BY TWO O'CLOCK!

GOOD HUNTING, BOYS!

Just after twelve noon, the door of Joe Doone's "cell" opened.

HERE'S YOUR DINNER, KID. I HOPE YOUR MATES PAY UP SOON. I WANT TO GO TO THE TEST MATCH IN NOTTINGHAM TO SEE THIS JOE DOONE THE CLARION IS ALWAYS ON ABOUT!

When the rest of the men heard about Joe, they growled that they would be after Marsh's blood.

SEE HIM? YOU CAN SEE HIM JUST NOW! I'M JOE DOONE! HERE'S MY M.C.C. PASS CARD TO PROVE IT!

WHAT? JUST WAIT TILL I TELL THE REST OF THE LADS!

THAT SKUNK NEVER TOLD US YOUR NAME, JOE, OR WE WOULD NEVER HAVE TOUCHED YOU!

WE DON'T MIND A BIT OF KIDNAPPING, BUT RUIN ENGLAND'S CHANCES IN THE TEST—NEVER!

WE'LL TAKE YOU ANYWHERE YOU WANT TO GO, JOE, AND JUST WAIT TILL WE SEE MARSH AGAIN—HE'LL BE SORRY FOR THIS!

The first ball in his first Test—and he's never played cricket before!

Joe and his bodyguard arrived at the Clarion office at two o'clock, and Ted Stevens rushed them into the room where Marsh was collecting his money.

PUT THAT MONEY BACK, MARSH!

AM I GLAD TO SEE YOU, JOE!

LEAVE MARSH TO US—WE'LL DEAL WITH HIM! WE'LL GO TO NOTTINGHAM WITH JOE TO SEE NOTHING MORE HAPPENS!

Next day, Joe was escorted to the cricket ground.

WE'LL GIVE YOU A CHEER, JOE!

PLAYERS AND OFFICIALS ONLY

THANKS, LADS! I'LL DO MY BEST FOR YOU!

WE'VE WON THE TOSS AND ARE BATTING. YOU'RE LAST MAN IN, DOONE, SO TRY NOT TO GET NERVOUS WHILE YOU'RE WAITING.

Joe took the England captain's words to heart. He didn't get nervous!

WAKE UP, DOONE— IT'S YOUR TURN TO BAT!

HEH? WASSAT?

GOOD LUCK, LAD! WATCH FOR THE GOOGLY!

GOOGLY? I THOUGHT THEY WERE ALL AUSTRALIANS!

N° 8 TOTAL
43 266
WICKETS
CAUGHT 9
BOWLED

Joe prepared to face his first-ever ball in a cricket match.

THAT'S AN ODD GUARD YOU'RE TAKING, COBBER!

" Where did they dig this clown up? He's hopeless!"

Can Joe keep up the good work? You'll find the answer on page 157!

Britain's Brightest Boys' Paper

THE **Victor**

EVERY MONDAY

Price 5d

No. 208
FEB. 13th
1965

FOUR KILLS FOR THE LITTLE SHIPS

On 24th October, 1943, thirty German E-boats attempted to attack a British convoy in the North Sea. They reached the convoy, but they in turn were attacked by motor gun boats— Britain's little ships.

MGB 110

The British convoy was first spotted by a German reconnaissance plane.

A BRITISH CONVOY! THE NAVY WILL BE GLAD TO HEAR ABOUT THIS!

At German Naval H.Q.

ONE OF OUR RECONNAISSANCE PLANES HAS SPOTTED A BRITISH CONVOY. TWO FLOTILLAS OF E-BOATS WILL SET OUT AND DESTROY IT.

The E-boats set out.

CONTINUED ON BACK PAGE

The remaining E-boats ran for home. None of the British boats was lost, but four E-boats were sunk and others damaged. The British convoy proceeded on its way.

SEE PAGE 140 for the next colour cover story.

PRINTED AND PUBLISHED IN GREAT BRITAIN BY D. C. THOMSON & CO., LTD., AND JOHN LENG & CO., LTD., 12 FETTER LANE, FLEET STREET, LONDON, E.C.4. © D. C. THOMSON & CO., LTD. 1965.

The deadly hands of Richard Falk reach out—and a swimming pool becomes a place of peril.

VOLTS of VENGEANCE

Mistaken for his double, a gangster called Dillingham, Richard Falk was sent to the electric chair —but he survived. The current had stored up in his body, and now he had to wear thick gloves to prevent anyone he touched being electrocuted. On the trail of the Dillingham gang, Falk was in San Francisco, looking for a mobster named Banion.

BLAST! BANION IS GOING AWAY! WELL, AT LEAST I'LL BE ABLE TO GET IN FOR A PROWL AROUND.

HMMM, NO TREES AND NO FOOTHOLDS! I'LL HAVE TO USE THESE CABLES TO GET OVER THE WALL.

THIS WILL CHARGE ME UP NICELY AT THE SAME TIME.

GOOD. NO-ONE IS IN SIGHT. I'LL BE ABLE TO GET INTO THE HOUSE.

THERE ARE NO DOCUMENTS THAT WOULD HELP ME SMASH BANION'S RACKET. I'LL HAVE A LOOK ROUND THE GROUNDS.

HULLO, THAT'S TONY MORELLO IN THE POOL. HE'S BANION'S RIGHT HAND MAN. HERE'S A CHANCE.

DON'T LOOK FOR A FEW MINUTES MORE, MORELLO!

The water conducted Falk's fantastic power, and Morello took a big enough electric shock to knock him out.

GOT YOU!

OUT YOU COME. THAT SHOCK SHOULD KEEP YOU QUIET FOR FIFTEEN MINUTES OR SO.

In a small pavilion nearby, Falk found Morello's clothes, and rummaged through them.

HULLO, THIS IS INTERESTING. I'LL TAKE A QUICK COPY AND STUDY IT MORE CAREFULLY LATER.

Only Falk can foil the power station plot.

His business finished, Falk left by the same way he had entered.

Ten minutes later, Morello came round, with a throbbing head, and wondering what had suddenly made him black out!

Later, in Falk's rented apartment.

LET'S SEE WHAT'S HERE, A DIAGRAM OF THE CITY POWER-HOUSE, A TIME—11.50 P.M. TONIGHT, AND HERE'S A LIST OF BANKS, STORES, GAMBLING JOINTS AND OFFICES. AH, HERE'S SOMETHING ELSE—RENDEZVOUS MAC'S CLUB, 12.30.

I THINK I SEE IT. BANION MEANS TO SHUT OFF THE CITY'S LIGHTS AT 11.50, WHEN HIS MEN WILL ROB THESE PLACES ON THE LIST. THEN THEY'LL ALL MEET AT MAC'S CLUB FORTY MINUTES LATER. THE COP'S WILL BE HELPLESS IN THE DARK, UNLESS THEY'RE WARNED.

HELLO, POLICE? NEVER MIND WHO'S SPEAKING. LISTEN, THERE'S GOING TO BE AN OUTBREAK OF ROBBERIES AT 11.50 TONIGHT. IT'S SAM BANION'S GANG. IF YOU POST MEN AT ALL THESE PLACES, YOU'LL CATCH THEM RED-HANDED. RIGHT, HERE'S THE LIST—

That night.

NOW FOR THE POWER STATION. I'LL KEEP GUARD THERE MYSELF.

THIS IS MY WAY IN. NOBODY WILL THINK OF LOOKING UP!

TYPE B TRANSFORMER

KEEP CLEAR HIGH VOLTAGE

OVER I GO. THERE'S A HANDY SKYLIGHT.

GOOD, THERE'S ONLY ONE MAN ON DUTY. NOW, IF ONLY I CAN GET DOWN THERE UNNOTICED—

SORRY I HAVE TO DO THIS, CHUM, BUT I WANT TO TAKE YOUR PLACE.

Banion holds the key to Falk's final vengeance!

I'D BETTER HURRY. THEY'LL BE HERE IN TEN MINUTES.

Ten minutes later.

DON'T TRY ANY FUNNY STUFF, YOU. DO AS YOU'RE TOLD AND YOU'LL COME TO NO HARM. NOW, SHUT OFF THE MAIN SWITCH.

YEAH, SURE—ANYTHING YOU SAY!

At 11.50 exactly, the lights of San Francisco went out.

GOOD. NOW COME AWAY FROM THERE.

I CAN'T. MY JACKET'S CAUGHT IN THE SWITCH LEVER.

Falk stood with his hands on the terminal.

I'LL FREE YOU—AGGH!

Each man came up to investigate his comrade's plight, and each one fell under Falk's deadly touch, until Morello himself lay unconscious at the Human Battery's feet.

Then Falk switched on the city lights again, and Banion's men were caught red-handed! Soon they were all locked up.

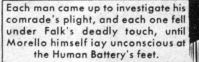
Half an hour after midnight.

NOW TO KEEP THE RENDEZVOUS WITH MR SAM BANION!

NEVER MIND WHO I AM, BANION. TELL ME WHO YOUR BOSS IS, AND WHERE I CAN FIND HIM.

IT'S DILLINGHAM, IN NEW YORK—HIS ADDRESS IS IN MY POCKET—NOW LET ME GO, PLEASE!

THAT'S BANION OUT OF THE WAY. AT LAST, I'M GETTING NEAR THE END OF THE TRAIL. I'VE FOUND MY WAY TO DILLINGHAM, AND MY FINAL VENGEANCE!

PRIVATE

Morgyn is attacked—by one of his friends!

SEVEN TRAILS TO MORGYN THE MIGHTY

When six hunters and their Zulu tracker came to shoot big game in the Ompopo Valley in Africa, they found that Morgyn the Mighty, the strongest man in the world, had driven most of the animals out of the valley to save their lives. In a fury, the seven men decided to hunt Morgyn instead. But Morgyn proved a difficult prey and had already got rid of three of the hunters. One day Morgyn was walking through the jungle when—

WHAT'S THAT MEAT DOING THERE? I MUST INVESTIGATE.

POISONED! THIS MEAT HAS BEEN TREATED IN SOME WAY. THE HUNTERS MUST BE RESPONSIBLE FOR THIS! I MUST BURN IT!

THAT POISON DOESN'T SMELL LIKE ANY I KNOW. I WONDER WHAT EFFECT IT WILL HAVE ON WHATEVER ANIMAL TAKES IT?

TWO LIONS HAVE BEEN HERE! I HOPE THEY DIDN'T EAT ANY OF THE MEAT!

AH! THERE'S SIMBA.

HE'S BEHAVING STRANGELY. WHY SHOULD HE SNARL AT ME? I'M HIS FRIEND.

WHAT CAN BE WRONG WITH HIM?

" I'll have to kill him."

I'LL HAVE TO KILL HIM. HE IS UNABLE TO THINK PROPERLY. IT MUST BE THE EFFECT OF THE POISON. IT MAKES ANIMALS FEROCIOUS!

DIE, SIMBA, OLD FRIEND!

I MUST FIND THE MAN WHO THOUGHT OF THIS PLAN. I EXPECT I'LL FIND HIM AT THE HUNTERS' CAMP!

I MIGHT BE ABLE TO OVERHEAR SOMETHING FROM UP THIS TREE.

THERE THEY ARE!

IF THE POISONED MEAT HAS BEEN TAKEN THAT WILD MAN SHOULD BE DEAD BY NOW. I'LL BET HE GOT A SHOCK WHEN ONE OF HIS LION FRIENDS ATTACKED HIM.

YES, THAT WAS A GREAT PLAN OF YOURS, MUELLER.

YES, BUT WE MUST GO OUT TOMORROW AND MAKE SURE THAT THE POISON HAS BEEN TAKEN.

SO IT WAS MUELLER WHO WAS RESPONSIBLE FOR THIS FIENDISH PLAN. I WILL MAKE HIM PAY FOR IT AND I KNOW HOW.

Next morning—

THERE THEY GO. I WILL GO AHEAD NOW WITH MY PLAN.

Soon—

LOOK! THE MEAT HAS BEEN BURNT.

YES, BUT LOOK AT THE LIONS' TRACKS. YOUR PLAN HAS WORKED, MUELLER, FOR THE LIONS WOULD NOT COME HERE IF THERE WAS A FIRE. IT MUST HAVE EATEN SOME OF THE MEAT BEFORE THE REST WAS BURNED. IT WILL HAVE BEEN AFFECTED BY THE POISON.

The end of an evil man!

Within moments Mueller lay dead, a victim of his own fiendish plot!

CONTINUED ON PAGE 136 — Morgyn is captured!

Sneak-thief Lemmy Crale twice outwits Sergeant Samson—but the third time he's not so lucky!

SERGEANT SAMSON'S SCRAPBOOK

MY NAME IS SAMSON AND I'M A COP. MY PALS CALL ME SCRAPPER BECAUSE I LIKE A GOOD FIGHT. LEMMY CRALE WAS A SNEAK-THIEF WHO GAVE ME THE RUN-AROUND FOR A TIME. BUT LEMMY'S LUCK RAN OUT EVENTUALLY.

I first met Lemmy when I was on patrol one night—

HEY! WHAT ARE YOU UP TO?

THAT'LL HOLD THE FLATFOOT!

DRINK COOLA & POP

OOOF!

WOW! THAT NEARLY RATTLED ALL MY TEETH LOOSE! AND THE BLIGHTER'S GOT AWAY! BUT I'LL KNOW HIS UGLY MUG IF I SEE HIM AGAIN.

I didn't know Lemmy's name at that time, but I kept my eyes open for him. My chance came when I was out in a patrol car one night—

PROCEED TO CARVER STREET. A PASSER-BY HAS REPORTED SUSPICIOUS LIGHTS IN AN OFFICE BUILDING THERE.

STEP ON IT. WE'RE NOT FAR FROM CARVER STREET.

Two minutes later we coasted silently to a stop in Carver Street—

YES, THERE'S SOMEBODY INSIDE. YOU GO AND COVER THE REAR ENTRANCE. I'LL TAKE THE FRONT.

POLIC

The front door of the office had been forced open—

SOME BRIGHT BOY AFTER THE PETTY CASH! I'LL SWITCH THE LIGHT ON.

WELL, WELL! THE SMART LAD WHO TRIPPED ME UP!

COR! THAT BIG FLATFOOT AGAIN! ALL RIGHT, SARGE, IT'S A FAIR COP.

BRR! IT'S COLD!

DON'T WORRY, MATE, WE'LL SOON HAVE YOU IN A NICE WARM CELL.

"He's a thief! Stop him, Matt!"

I couldn't see what Lemmy was up to. I thought he was fastening his jacket—but he was slipping on a set of knuckledusters—

GET IN THE CAR—OUCH!

LAUGH THAT OFF, COPPER!

When I came to, my driver had just come round to see what was going on—

WHAT HAPPENED, SARGE?

I SHOULD HAVE KNOWN BETTER! I THOUGHT HE'D THROWN HIS HAND IN. THEN HE THREW A PUNCH AT ME, INSTEAD! AND THAT'S THE SECOND TIME HE'S SEEN ME OFF!

My police pals pulled my leg about the way I'd been floored—particularly as I was preparing for a local boxing tournament—

WILL YOUR SORE JAW BE BETTER IN TIME FOR THE TOURNAMENT, SARGE?

FUNNY MAN! MY JAW'S ALL RIGHT. AND THE NEXT TIME I SEE THAT TWISTER, HE'LL BE AT THE RECEIVING END!

Lemmy also had plans for the night of the tournament—

SPORTS SPECIAL
POLICE SERGEANT FAVOURITE TO WIN AMATEUR HEAVYWEIGHT TITLE AT HAMPTON CLUB

THERE'LL BE NICE PICKINGS AT THE HAMPTON CLUB. AND THAT FLATFOOT WILL BE OUT OF THE WAY IN THE RING.

I was to fight Matt Brady, a local miner. I forgot about crooks and concentrated on boxing—

SAMSON'S HEADING FOR THE RING. WE'LL HANG ON A FEW MINUTES, MATT.

PLAYING A WAITING GAME, EH?

WE'LL LET SAMSON COOL HIS HEELS IN THE RING FOR A BIT. A WAIT BEFORE THE FIGHT SOMETIMES GETS A BOXER JUMPY.

I DON'T THINK IT'LL WORK, NOT WITH SAMSON, BUT I'M WILLING TO TRY ANYTHING THAT MIGHT SOFTEN UP THAT BIG COPPER.

Lemmy made his appearance through a window in the dressing-room—

I CAN HEAR THE CROWD YELLING IN THE HALL. THE BIG FIGHT IS ABOUT TO START. THAT'LL KEEP SAMSON OUT OF THE WAY WHILE I MAKE A QUICK HAUL!

NOT BAD, SO FAR! NOW FOR THE NEXT DRESSING-ROOM!

But Matt and his seconds were just leaving the other dressing room—

TIME WE WERE MOVING, MATT.

YES, WE CAN'T KEEP THE CROWD WAITING ANY LONGER.

HEY! WHO ARE YOU? WHAT ARE YOU DOING HERE?

LOOK AT THE LOOT! HE'S A THIEF! STOP HIM, MATT.

The two-fisted vengeance of Sergeant Samson!

Lemmy acted fast— HE'S LAID MATT OUT! GET HIM!

DOORKEEPER! STOP THAT MAN!

TO THE RING

THIS WAY'S MY ONLY HOPE.

I was waiting in the ring— STOP HIM! HE'S A THIEF AND HE'S LAID OUT MATT BRADY!

BLIMEY, WHAT'S THIS I'VE GOT MYSELF INTO?

TEACH THE THIEF A LESSON!

HELP! THEY'LL TEAR ME APART!

YES, AND TEACH HIM TO LEAVE OUR BOXERS ALONE!

UP YOU COME, CHUMMY!

KEEP THEM OFF ME!

THROW HIM BACK! HE'S RUINED OUR NIGHT'S BOXING!

I'VE BEEN WANTING TO MEET YOU FOR A LONG TIME, LEMMY. WELL, YOU'VE PUT MATT BRADY OUT, SO YOU CAN TAKE HIS PLACE. YOU CAN BOX AN EXHIBITION BOUT WITH ME.

WHAT? ARE YOU KIDDING?

GO THREE ROUNDS WITH ME UP HERE—OR I'LL CHUCK YOU BACK INTO THE CROWD.

YOU WOULDN'T DO THAT? YEAH, YOU WOULD, TOO. ALL RIGHT, GIVE ME THE GLOVES!

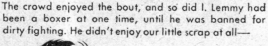

The crowd enjoyed the bout, and so did I. Lemmy had been a boxer at one time, until he was banned for dirty fighting. He didn't enjoy our little scrap at all—

I'M GLAD I DIDN'T FIGHT YOU TONIGHT, SAMSON. YOU MUST HAVE BEEN IN A REAL SCRAPPING MOOD!

I'M COMING WITH YOU, BOYS. I WANT TO MAKE SURE MY OPPONENT WAKES UP IN A CELL!

A pilot and mechanic of the Royal Flying Corps spot the position where a German attack is going to be made — but their information may be too late!

WHEN THE SHOT AND THE SHELL WERE FLYING

After a fighting withdrawal from Mons in the face of overwhelming German forces, the British Army found itself preparing for a last stand only a few miles from Paris. Further retreat was out of the question and, for Bob Millar and his comrades of the Coldstream Guards, this looked like the end of the road. Their orders were to stay where they were and to fight to the last man.

WELL, THIS IS IT, BOB. EITHER WE LICK THEM OR THIS IS WHERE THEY'LL BURY OUR BONES!

LOOKS LIKE IT, FRED. BUT WHY HAVEN'T THE GERMANS ATTACKED US? THEIR BEST CHANCE WAS TO HIT US BEFORE WE'D FINISHED DIGGING OUR TRENCHES.

Meanwhile, at a British airfield.

OUR PATROLS HAVE LOST CONTACT WITH THE ENEMY. CAN YOU FLY A RECONNAISSANCE FOR US?

OUR TROOPS ARE PRETTY THIN ON THE GROUND SO IT WOULD BE A BIG HELP IF WE COULD KNOW WHERE TO EXPECT THE MAIN GERMAN ATTACK. DO YOUR BEST, OLD FELLOW.

CERTAINLY, OLD BOY. I'VE GOT A TWO-SEATER PLANE READY TO TAKE THE AIR.

WE'LL WATCH FOR TROOP MOVEMENTS AND CONCENTRATIONS. THEY WON'T BE ABLE TO CONCEAL THEM FROM US— YOU CAN SEE EVERYTHING FROM THE AIR.

CONTACT!

IT LOOKS PRETTY QUIET DOWN BELOW, SIR. USUALLY SOME HOPEFUL BLOKE TAKES A POT AT US WITH HIS RIFLE BEFORE WE'VE COME THIS FAR!

IT'S TOO QUIET, MILLARD. THAT'S WHAT IS WORRYING THE ARMY CHAPS. KEEP YOUR EYES SKINNED.

SOMETHING DEAD AHEAD, SIR.

CAVALRY, SIR! JUST CAVALRY!

IT DOESN'T MAKE SENSE, MILLARD. TWO DAYS AGO THERE WAS INFANTRY AND ARTILLERY SWARMING ALL OVER THIS AREA. WE'D BETTER FLY ON AND SEE WHAT'S GOING ON.

AMIENS COMING UP ON OUR LEFT, SIR!

I'VE SPOTTED THEM. WE'LL GO DOWN FOR A CLOSER LOOK.

CRIKEY! LOOK AT THOSE TROOPS AND VEHICLES! IT MUST BE A WHOLE ARMY CORPS ON THE MOVE!

"We must get back at once!"

DONNER-WETTER!

THAT PUT THE WIND UP THEM, SIR! LET'S DO IT AGAIN!

NOT THIS TRIP, MILLARD. THE GERMAN RIGHT WING IS MARCHING SOUTH-EAST, RIGHT ACROSS THE FRONT OF OUR ARMY. WE MUST GET BACK AT ONCE AND MAKE OUR REPORT!

WE'RE LOSING HEIGHT, SIR! WHAT'S WRONG?

THE ENGINE IS OVERHEATING.. I'LL PUT HER DOWN SOMEWHERE AND YOU CAN TAKE A LOOK.

OIL-PIPE FRACTURED, SIR. I CAN DO A TEMPORARY JOB WITH TAPE IN A MATTER OF MINUTES!

Minutes later.

LOOK OUT, MILLARD! THEY'RE ON TO US!

SWITCH ON, SIR, AND I'LL GIVE HER A SWING!

TAKE OFF, SIR! TAKE OFF!

In the nick of time the intrepid airmen took off. Minutes later the vital information was in the hands of the British Commander.

TO FRENCH HIGH COMMAND. FOR GENERAL JOFFRE—IMMEDIATE! AIR-RECONNAISSANCE REVEALS ENEMY LEFT WING TURNING SOUTH-EAST ACROSS BRITISH FRONT. OBVIOUS HIS INTENTION TO ROLL-UP FRENCH MAIN ARMY AND ENCIRCLE PARIS.

The French were forewarned, but could not prevent the blow falling. German troops in overwhelming numbers crossed the Marne and a fierce battle raged.

" Allied Advance!"

THEY ARE PUSHING US BACK, GENERAL. OUR MEN CANNOT HOLD THEM!

IF ONLY I HAD JUST ONE ARMY CORPS MORE. I WOULD HURL IT UPON THEIR LEFT-FLANK AND THROW THEM INTO CONFUSION!

BUT THERE IS NO SUCH CORPS TO HAND, GENERAL! WE CAN SPARE NO MEN FROM THIS FLANK—NOT A SINGLE ONE!

In Paris, the danger was clearly recognised, and General Gellieni, commanding the Paris garrison, racked his brains for means of striking a blow for France.

WE HAVE A WHOLE ARMY HERE IN PARIS. IF THE GERMANS BREAK OUR FRONT-LINE WE WILL STILL SMASH THEM.

AN ARMY, YES! BUT NO TRANSPORT, MY GOOD D'AUDOBON! IF OUR MEN MUST MARCH THEN THEY MAY AS WELL STAY HERE, FOR THEY COULD NOT MARCH ANYWHERE QUICKLY ENOUGH TO BE OF ANY ASSISTANCE!

TRANSPORTATION—THAT IS WHAT I REQUIRE. BUT—NOM D'UN NOM! PARIS IS FULL OF TRANSPORTATION! THE SOLUTION STARES ME IN THE FACE!

INTO THE STREETS WITH YOU! SEIZE ME TAXI-CABS, AUTOMOBILES, BICYCLES—ANYTHING THAT GOES UPON WHEELS! WE MARCH TO MEAUX, AND THERE, IF THE BON DIEU PERMITS—WE WILL STRIKE THESE GERMANS SUCH A BLOW AS THEY WILL NEVER FORGET!

The citizens of Paris beheld a most amazing sight as the garrison seized vehicles of every type and packed them with troops.

Like an avalanche, the hurriedly-assembled army fell upon Meaux.

The German flank, weakened by the withdrawal of troops for the main assault, could not withstand the sudden onslaught. By nightfall the French had broken through and the German line was in full retreat.

Everywhere the Allies advanced. British guns hammered the retreating enemy. British troops marched, overjoyed that the days of weary retreat were over. But Bob Millar, like many another soldier, asked himself a question.

WELL, PARIS IS SAVED—BUT WHAT NOW? HOW MUCH LONGER BEFORE THE GERMANS ARE LICKED?

The boyhood of international football's blond bombshell—the one and only Denis Law!

WHEN HE WAS A BOY—

Denis Law

DYNAMIC, SCOTS-BORN FOOTBALLER, DENIS LAW, HAS BEEN THE BRAINS OF THE HUDDERSFIELD, MANCHESTER CITY AND ITALIAN TORINO TEAMS IN RECENT YEARS. HE STARS REGULARLY FOR HIS COUNTRY.

Denis's home town is Aberdeen, where his father is a trawlerman.

He was born with a squint in his right eye.

I'M AFRAID WE'LL HAVE TO GIVE YOU SPECTACLES, SON.

But Denis knew what he wanted to be, glasses or no glasses!

I'M GOING TO SEA WHEN I GROW UP.

I WANT TO BE AN ENGINE DRIVER

WELL, I'M GOING TO BE A FOOTBALLER, ONE DAY, AND MAYBE PLAY FOR SCOTLAND.

He played left-back, left-half and inside-left for Powis Junior Secondary School.

WELL, HERE'S HOPING I CAN SEE THE BALL!

In order to toughen his feet, Denis put in hours of practice bare-footed.

His greatest honour while he was still at school was to be chosen as reserve to the Scottish Under-14 side against Ireland, at Belfast.

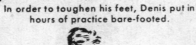

The wandering boy from Aberdeen!

Denis was always a small youngster, but good food helped to keep him strong and fit.

COME ON, DENIS, YOU'LL HAVE TO EAT PLENTY IF YOU WANT TO MAKE FOOTBALL YOUR CAREER

Soon, Denis had a big chance to go South.

I WANT DENIS DOWN AT HUDDERSFIELD. HE'LL BE ON THE GROUND STAFF AT FIRST, BUT I THINK HE'LL MAKE THE GRADE AS A PLAYER VERY SOON.

So Denis went to Huddersfield. At first, he felt out of place, training alongside bigger, fitter men.

Though he was the frailest of the ground staff, Denis got the job of rolling the ground. This helped to put pounds on him.

Huddersfield sent 15-year-old Denis back to Aberdeen for an eye operation, which was completely successful in straightening his right eye.

IT'S STRAIGHT! MY EYE'S STRAIGHT! NOW I CAN REALLY BE A FOOTBALLER!

Under his club's training programme, Denis started to learn a trade—painting. He had to attend Technical College, too. But this reminded him too much of school, so he gave up and concentrated on football.

In season 1956-57, Denis played his first match for the 1st XI, on Christmas Eve.

HERE GOES—MY FIRST GAME FOR THE FIRST TEAM. WHAT A CHRISTMAS PRESENT!

In February 1957, Denis signed professional forms for his club. He had realised his ambition. Now he was a full-time footballer.

Denis played a hard, strong-tackling game which led to several injuries.

NOT ANOTHER INJURY, DENIS?

TAILOR

At 18, Denis was picked to play for Scotland. He played a great game and scored a goal for his country. Since then, Denis has been going from strength to strength, and last season he was snapped up by the Italian team, Torino.

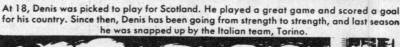

I FLEW WITH BRADDOCK

THAT'S ENOUGH FOR THIS AFTERNOON, GEORGE. I NEED A COUPLE OF GASKETS FOR MY BIKE. HOW ABOUT A STROLL INTO TOWN?

GOOD IDEA, BRAD. I'VE FINISHED MY FLIGHT PLAN ANYWAY. WE'RE ALL SET FOR THE RAID.

SERGEANT MATT BRADDOCK, V.C., was the greatest pilot of the last war. This is the story of the famous book about him, written by George Bourne, his navigator. Braddock was to make a special mission to drop a big, new bomb, designed by Mr Smith, a brilliant scientist, on the Degen, Germany's new aircraft carrier. The Degen was a deadly threat to British shipping. Group Captain Mandeville, the commanding officer of Barminster R.A.F. station, had a terrific reputation as a flyer—but Braddock had discovered him to be a fraud. The C.O. was jealous of Braddock, but had so far failed to have him taken off the Degen mission.

HERE COME MANDEVILLE AND PROUT, ONE OF HIS "YES MEN".

QUITE AN ENTOURAGE. MY LACE IS UNTIED. WALK ON, BRAD. I WON'T BE A SECOND.

WHAT'S BRAD DOING? HAS HE GONE MAD?

SO THAT'S IT. THAT'S A CAPTURED GERMAN PLANE. BRAD THOUGHT IT WAS GOING TO ATTACK.

Captured German planes were sometimes marked with roundels and flown by the R.A.F., to find out all about them.

SORRY I TREATED YOU ROUGH. I SAW THE ME 210 COMING AND THOUGHT IT WOULD START SHOOTING. I COULDN'T WARN YOU BECAUSE OF THE WORKMAN WITH THE DRILL.

THAT'S ALL RIGHT.

SORRY ABOUT THAT. HEAD ON, THERE WAS NO WAY OF TELLING IT WAS A CAPTURED MACHINE.

SO THAT'S YOUR EXPLANATION.

IT'S THE TRUTH. I THOUGHT THE GERMAN PLANE WAS GOING TO SHOOT UP THE ROAD.

HMM. COME, CHANG!

Later.

WELL, WE GOT WHAT WE WERE LOOKING FOR, GEORGE. AND IT WAS A FINE WALK. HULLO—WHAT'S THE RECEPTION COMMITTEE IN AID OF?

IT LOOKS LIKE TROUBLE, BRAD.

"You can tell that to the judge at the court-martial, Braddock."

SERGEANT BRADDOCK, I'VE HAD ORDERS TO PLACE YOU UNDER CLOSE ARREST.

AGAIN! WHAT HAVE I DONE THIS TIME?

YOU'LL BE CHARGED WITH ASSAULTING TWO SUPERIOR OFFICERS. IT'S A VERY GRAVE OFFENCE.

COME OFF IT! I THOUGHT I WAS SAVING THEIR LIVES.

YOU CAN EXPLAIN ALL THAT AT THE COURT-MARTIAL, BRADDOCK, MEANTIME IT'S THE COOLER FOR YOU. QUICK MARCH!

I'LL SEE WHAT I CAN DO, BRAD.

YOU WON'T BE ABLE TO DO MUCH. MANDEVILLE'S TOO CUNNING.

MANDEVILLE'S GOT ME WHERE HE WANTS ME, NOW. WITH PROUT TO BACK HIM UP, HE'LL PRESENT A STRONG CASE. IT'S A PERFECT FRAME-UP!

Next day.

I WANT TO HAVE A HEART TO HEART TALK WITH YOU CHAPS. UNFORTUNATELY, SERGEANT BRADDOCK WILL NOT FLY WITH YOU ON THIS RAID. HE IS UNDER ARREST AND WILL FACE A COURT-MARTIAL.

BUT HE ONLY TIPPED YOU OVER BECAUSE HE THOUGHT THE PLANE WAS A GERMAN RAIDER, SIR!

NO, BOURNE, THAT WAS JUST HIS EXCUSE. YOU WERE TOO FAR AWAY TO HEAR, BUT AS HE KNOCKED ME DOWN HE CALLED ME A DIRTY RAT. FLYING OFFICER PROUT WILL CONFIRM THAT. BUT ENOUGH OF THAT. TONIGHT, SQUADRON LEADER HOWERTH WILL TAKE BRADDOCK'S PLANE. I WAS HOPING TO FLY WITH YOU, BUT MY PLACE IS HERE. THAT'S ALL FOR NOW. THE FINAL BRIEFING WILL BE AT 1500 HOURS.

HE'S A CROOK AND HE'S YELLOW. HE'S FRAMED BRAD, BUT HE'S TOO WINDY TO FLY ON THE RAID HIMSELF.

THERE'S NOT MUCH WE CAN DO. MANDEVILLE SEEMS TO HOLD ALL THE ACES.

Later.

WELL, THERE IT GOES, GEORGE. I JUST HOPE WE CAN DELIVER IT WHERE IT WILL DO MOST DAMAGE.

ME TOO. A LOT DEPENDS ON HOWERTH. HE'S A GOOD PILOT, BUT HE'S NOT A PATCH ON BRADDOCK. HEY, WHAT ABOUT GOING ROUND TO THE JAIL? WE MIGHT SNEAK A WORD WITH BRAD.

I WAS HOPING YOU'D NIP ROUND. WHO'S GOING ON THE RAID TONIGHT?

HOWERTH. WE'VE GOT THE FINAL BRIEFING AT 1500 HOURS.

" Mr Braddock will be dropping my bomb."

THEN TELL HOWERTH HE MUST COME IN LOW. IT'S ESSENTIAL THAT HE FLIES NO HIGHER THAN 6000 FEET AND—

GET OUT OF IT, YOU HORRIBLE MEN!

OH, OH! HERE COMES FLIGHT SERGEANT GULL. WE'D BETTER HOP IT, BRAD. I'LL TELL HOWERTH.

Later, at the briefing.

WEATHER WILL BE CLEAR AND THE WIND STRENGTH—

WHERE'S MR BRADDOCK?

BRADDOCK IS UNDER ARREST ON A SERIOUS CHARGE.

I DON'T CARE IF HE'S UNDER ARREST ON A CHARGE OF MURDER! NOBODY ELSE IS GOING TO DROP MY BOMB!

THERE CAN BE NO RELEASE FOR BRADDOCK. I HAVE REPORTED THIS AFFAIR TO THE AIR OFFICER COMMANDING. HE AGREES THAT THE CHARGE IS TOO SERIOUS FOR BRADDOCK TO BE GIVEN MORE LATITUDE. EVEN THE COMMANDER IN CHIEF WOULDN'T INTERVENE.

WE SHALL SEE. CARRY ON WITH THE BRIEFING MEANTIME. BUT I HAVEN'T FINISHED WITH YOU YET!

After the briefing, Bourne and Howerth talked over the navigational and operational plan of the flight, and Bourne gave Howerth Braddock's message.

BRADDOCK SAYS THE ONLY WAY TO TACKLE THE JOB IS TO GO IN AT 6000 FEET.

THERE DOESN'T SEEM TO BE MUCH FUTURE IN ATTACKING AT 6000 FEET.

BRADDOCK NEVER CONSIDERED THE FUTURE AS LONG AS HE COULD DO THE JOB.

VERY WELL. WE SHALL GO IN AT 6000 FEET.

That evening.

I'VE TOLD YOU BEFORE, MR SMITH, I'M BUSY AND DON'T WISH TO BE DISTURBED. I KNOW YOU WISH TO WITNESS THE DEPARTURE OF THE BOMBER, BUT YOU WILL PLEASE STAY IN THE OFFICERS' MESS UNTIL YOU ARE FETCHED.

MR BRADDOCK WILL BE DROPPING MY BOMB. YOU WILL BE GETTING A SIGNAL ABOUT IT. THAT MIGHT BE IT ON THE PHONE NOW!

ADJUTANT, CRAXBY, SPEAKING.

TAKE A SIGNAL.

PLEASE DON'T HARP ON THE SUBJECT, MR SMITH. BRADDOCK IS UNDER ARREST AND WILL NOT BE RELEASED UNDER ANY CONSIDERATION.

OH, YES SIR. CERTAINLY, SIR.

WHAT'S GOING ON THERE, PROUT?

IT—IT'S FROM THE PRIME MINISTER HIMSELF!

I THINK YOU'LL FIND THAT'S THE SIGNAL I WAS TALKING ABOUT.

SGT. BRADDOCK WILL FLY ON TONIGHT'S MISSION. THE NAME OF THE OFFICER WHO SOUGHT TO PREVENT HIM FROM EXECUTING THE TASK FOR WHICH HE WAS CHOSEN WILL BE MADE KNOWN TO ME AT ONCE. P.M.

YOU'RE REALLY IN TROUBLE NOW, MANDEVILLE. I WARNED YOU. BUT YOU WERE TOO PIG-HEADED TO LISTEN.

WELL, DON'T JUST STAND THERE, PROUT. GO AND FETCH BRADDOCK FROM DETENTION.

" Dented " will signal the Degen's doom!

A few minutes later.

BRADDOCK WON'T COME, SIR. HE SAYS HE'S QUITE COMFORTABLE WHERE HE IS.

IF YOU WANT A JOB DONE ON THIS STATION, YOU HAVE TO DO IT YOURSELF.

WHAT'S THIS NONSENSE ABOUT STAYING IN JAIL, BRADDOCK? A SIGNAL HAS BEEN RECEIVED THAT YOU'RE TO GO ON THE MISSION TONIGHT.

NOT WITH A SERIOUS CHARGE HANGING OVER MY HEAD. I COULDN'T CONCENTRATE ON THE JOB.

I'M GOING TO WITHDRAW THE CHARGE.

IT SHOULD NEVER HAVE BEEN MADE, SHOULD IT?

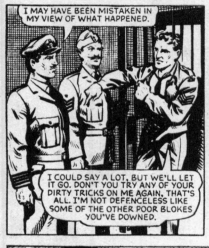

I MAY HAVE BEEN MISTAKEN IN MY VIEW OF WHAT HAPPENED.

I COULD SAY A LOT, BUT WE'LL LET IT GO. DON'T YOU TRY ANY OF YOUR DIRTY TRICKS ON ME AGAIN, THAT'S ALL. I'M NOT DEFENCELESS LIKE SOME OF THE OTHER POOR BLOKES YOU'VE DOWNED.

Later.

THEY TRIED TO STOP YOU DROPPING MY BOMB, MR BRADDOCK, BUT WE SOON PUT A STOP TO THAT NONSENSE!

YOU MAY BE SORRY YOU FETCHED ME OUT IF WE MISS THE TARGET.

OH NO, YOU WON'T DO THAT, THAT'S WHY WE PICKED YOU. COULD YOU LET US HAVE A WIRELESS SIGNAL IF YOU ARE SUCCESSFUL? IT WILL BE A LONG, ANXIOUS WAIT AS IT IS.

WE USUALLY SEND THE SIGNAL "OFF TARGET", BUT WE'LL HAVE A SPECIAL ONE TONIGHT. IF WE HIT THE DEGEN, WE'LL WIRELESS "DENTED"!

CONTROL CALLING F FOX, YOU CAN TAKE OFF NOW. GOOD LUCK!

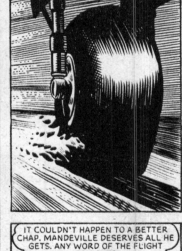

Then came disaster. A tyre burst!

I TAKE OFF MY HAT TO YOU, BRAD. I THOUGHT WE'D HAD IT THERE. HOW YOU MANAGED TO AVOID A CRASH BEATS ME!

Next morning.

LOOK, MANDEVILLE'S LEAVING!

HE'S LEAVING FOR GOOD, GEORGE, AND HE'S IN PLENTY TROUBLE. HE'S BEEN RELIEVED OF HIS COMMAND HERE AND THERE'S TO BE AN INQUIRY INTO HIS CAREER. THE BIG SHOTS WANT TO KNOW HOW HE REALLY GOT THOSE MEDALS OF HIS!

IT WAS A NEAR THING. WELL, YOU CAN GET TO BED NOW, CHAPS. THE RAID'S OFF FOR TONIGHT.

IT COULDN'T HAPPEN TO A BETTER CHAP. MANDEVILLE DESERVES ALL HE GETS. ANY WORD OF THE FLIGHT TONIGHT?

IT DEPENDS ON WHETHER OR NOT OUR RECONNAISSANCE PLANES CAN FIND THE DEGEN. TIME IS AGAINST US, GEORGE. WE'VE GOT TO FIND THE DEGEN SOON OR IT WILL BE TOO LATE!

CONTINUED ON PAGE 161 F Fox goes after the Degen — and the big bomb is ready.

The Rovers play a new centre-half—and he's there just to be fouled!

GORGEOUS GUS

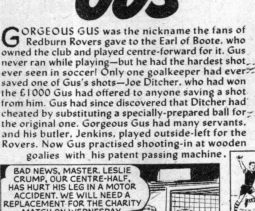

GORGEOUS GUS was the nickname the fans of Redburn Rovers gave to the Earl of Boote, who owned the club and played centre-forward for it. Gus never ran while playing—but he had the hardest shot ever seen in soccer! Only one goalkeeper had ever saved one of Gus's shots—Joe Ditcher, who had won the £1000 Gus had offered to anyone saving a shot from him. Gus had since discovered that Ditcher had cheated by substituting a specially-prepared ball for the original one. Gorgeous Gus had many servants, and his butler, Jenkins, played outside-left for the Rovers. Now Gus practised shooting-in at wooden goalies with his patent passing machine.

BAD NEWS, MASTER. LESLIE CRUMP, OUR CENTRE-HALF, HAS HURT HIS LEG IN A MOTOR ACCIDENT. WE WILL NEED A REPLACEMENT FOR THE CHARITY MATCH ON WEDNESDAY.

TELL BULL RAWLINGS TO REPORT TO ME IN MY OFFICE IN HALF AN HOUR.

Bull Rawlings had been the dirtiest player in football, before Gorgeous Gus had paid £20,000 for his transfer to the Rovers. But Gus had paid this large fee so that he could keep Rawlings out of the game. Now Bull earned his wages by picking up litter.

EVERY MAN IS ENTITLED TO A SECOND CHANCE, RAWLINGS, AND I'VE DECIDED TO GIVE YOU ONE. YOU WILL START TRAINING FOR THE MATCH ON WEDNESDAY AGAINST THE ALL-ENGLAND GIANTS. BUT I WARN YOU, ANY SIGN OF BAD TEMPER OR DIRTY TACTICS, AND YOU'LL BE OUT OF FOOTBALL FOR GOOD.

GEE THANKS, YOUR LORDSHIP. YOU WON'T REGRET IT. I WON'T LET YOU DOWN!

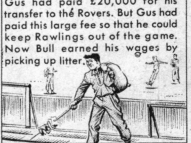

YES, I ALWAYS BELIEVE IN GIVING A MAN A SECOND CHANCE, BUT RAWLINGS HAS NO IDEA JUST HOW SEVERE HIS TEST WILL BE!

On Wednesday night.

GOSH, NO WONDER THEY CALL THEM THE ALL-ENGLAND GIANTS! OLD GUS MUST HAVE PICKED ALL THE BIGGEST PLAYERS IN THE FIRST DIVISION FOR THIS SELECT SIDE.

The match was only minutes old when the Giants started throwing their weight about.

NOT OFTEN BULL GETS A FOUL IN HIS FAVOUR. WATCH HIM TURN ON THE DIRTY STUFF NOW!

GOOD, THEY ARE PUTTING MY INSTRUCTIONS INTO OPERATION. RAWLINGS IS GOING TO HAVE A ROUGH PASSAGE. HE'LL DO WELL IF HE PASSES THIS TEST.

Bull was fouled time and time again by the Giants, but always came up smiling.

A FIRST-CLASS PASS, RAWLINGS—AND A WELL TAKEN GOAL!

Later

BULL'S PLAYING GREAT FOOTBALL, NOW THAT HE'S LEARNING TO KEEP HIS TEMPER.

A SHREWD PASS, RAWLINGS, VERY SHREWD INDEED!

" It's Joe Ditcher, the only goalie Gorgeous Gus couldn't beat!"

WHERE'S THE BALL? I—OOPS!

THE POOR CHAP HAS CONCUSSION BY THE LOOK OF HIM. SEND FOR MY PERSONAL PHYSICIAN RIGHT AWAY, EDWARDS. OH—AND ASK MY SECRETARY TO REPORT TO ME HERE. I HAVE MORE WORK TO DO.

PROPER CARD, OUR GORGEOUS GUS, AIN'T HE, FRED? MAKES HIMSELF RIGHT AT HOME.

LOOK, IT'S JOE DITCHER, THE ONLY GOALIE GORGEOUS GUS COULDN'T BEAT!

HEY, MISTER, THIS IS ONLY A CHARITY MATCH. THERE'S NO REASON WHY THE GIANTS SHOULD PLAY WITH ONLY TEN MEN. HOW ABOUT LETTING ME GO IN GOAL FOR THEM?

I'M VERY BUSY, MY MAN, AND DISLIKE BEING INTERRUPTED IN THIS WAY.

YOU'RE WINDY, THAT'S YOUR TROUBLE. YOU KNOW IF I GO IN GOAL I'LL SHOW YOU UP, YOU'LL NEVER SCORE!

I HAVE NO FEELINGS IN THE MATTER WHATSOEVER. IF YOU WISH TO KEEP GOAL FOR THE GIANTS, YOU HAVE MY PERMISSION

Later.

GREAT SAVE, DITCHER! WHAT A GOALIE! NO WONDER GUS IS SCARED TO COME ON AGAINST HIM.

NO, HE ISN'T. LOOK, HE'S GETTING TO HIS FEET!

NOW WE'LL SEE SOMETHING!

The fans did not have long to wait to see the duel between Gus and Joe Ditcher— and Gus failed miserably!

TUT, WHAT CAN HAVE GONE WRONG?

YAH! YOU'RE FRIGHTENED TO HIT THE BALL TO ME.

Time and time again, Gus failed to score from easy positions. His shooting ability seemed to have left him now he was faced with Joe Ditcher. The reformed Bull Rawlings was the star of the match, which ended with the Rovers winning 2-0, but still Gus had not beaten Ditcher.

SEE, I'VE GOT A JINX ON GORGEOUS GUS. HE'LL NEVER SCORE AGAINST ME!

WHAT WAS WRONG, SIR?

I'LL EXPLAIN LATER, JENKINS.

In the "Royal Pavilion," Gus's private dressing-room.

THAT'S THE REASON FOR MY POOR SHOOTING, JENKINS. THE BOOT IS BURST. I REALISED THAT, BUT DELIBERATELY DIDN'T DO ANYTHING ABOUT IT. THAT FELLOW DITCHER IS HEADING FOR A FALL, AND THE HIGHER HE GOES THE HARDER HE'LL FALL!

I WOULDN'T BE IN MR JOE DITCHER'S FOOTBALL BOOTS THIS SATURDAY FOR ANYTHING, SIR. THE CHAMPIONSHIP DECIDER BETWEEN THE ROVERS AND WINGTON CITY SHOULD BE VERY INTERESTING— VERY INTERESTING INDEED!

CONTINUED ON PAGE 165 The Rovers take the field with ten men in the championship decider —— and Gus is missing

Morgyn falls into the evil clutches of the remaining hunters!

SEVEN TRAILS TO MORGYN THE MIGHTY

" I won't be able to control them now!"

Will the remaining two hunters be able to finish Morgyn? Find out ON PAGE 148

Alf wins a cuckoo clock — and a gold medal!

THE TOUGH OF THE TRACK

IT ALL DEPENDS ON THE RUN-IN.

TUPPAIRE! TUPPAIRE!

Alf Tupper, the runner from the back streets of Greystone, who was known as the Tough of the Track, had hitch-hiked to Brussels to join the British team for the European Games. He had received his invitation too late to travel with the official party. Arriving in Brussels, he found his place had been taken and, rather than watch, he had taken part in a small sports meeting, winning the 1500 metres. He then entered the 400 metres hurdles and was level with another runner going over the last hurdle.

MADE IT!

WELL RUN, MONSIEUR TUPPAIRE! HERE IS YOUR PRIZE.

A CUCKOO CLOCK!

COO, THAT'S A BIG BLOKE! HE MUST WEIGH TWENTY STONES.

A few minutes later, Commander Churcher, one of the officials of the British team in the European Games, came running over to Alf.

TUPPER, WE NEED YOU AT THE EUROPEAN GAMES. WHITTINGTON PULLED A MUSCLE DOING EXERCISES IN THE DRESSING-ROOM. YOU'LL HAVE TO RUN IN THE 1500 METRES.

WHY, COMMANDER CHURCHER! THIS IS MY LUCKY DAY!

BUT YOU'VE BEEN RUNNING ALREADY! YOU'LL HAVE TAKEN TOO MUCH OUT OF YOURSELF!

NOT ME! I'M JUST LOOSENED UP NICELY!

Alf said goodbye to the organiser of the sports and Commander Churcher drove him to the European Games stadium.

COO, THIS IS A BIT BIGGER THAN THE FOOTBALL GROUND!

HERE'S A TEAM SINGLET, TUPPER.

I CAN'T WEAR THIS! IT'S FAR TOO BIG!

WELL, IT'S THE ONLY ONE WE'VE GOT LEFT.

I'LL WEAR ME OWN SINGLET.

THAT RAG!

CONTINUED ON PAGE 171 Alf wins the star prize at the Ixton Park Sports — a piano!

"I FLEW WITH BRADDOCK" — THE BIG THRILL STORY OF THE AIR WAR IS TOLD IN EXCITING PICTURES *INSIDE!*

THE VICTOR

EVERY MONDAY

Price 4½d.

No. 16
JUNE 10th
1961

Fast and tremendously powerful, the German battleship "Tirpitz" was a constant menace to British shipping. When British Intelligence heard that she was lying in Alten Fiord, in Norway, it was decided to end the menace once and for all. Early one morning in September, 1944, R.A.F. Lancasters landed at the Russian aerodrome of Yagodnik after a nightmare journey. Alten Fiord was out of range of the British bombers from Britain, so it was decided to strike from Russia.

YAGODNIK AT LAST. I HOPE THE OTHER LADS MAKE IT.

THEY MAY HAVE TROUBLE, SKIPPER. BEING SO NEAR THE NORTH POLE, ALL OUR COMPASSES HAVE GONE HAYWIRE.

THE END OF THE TIRPITZ

GOOD NEWS FOR YOU, COMRADES. THE 20 MISSING AIRCRAFT HAVE LANDED SAFELY AT OTHER DROMES. THOSE THAT CAN BE REPAIRED WILL BE RUSHED HERE BEFORE THE RAID.

WHAT A CAPER! WE'VE GOT TO SERVICE THESE CRATES OURSELVES.

YES, AND IT'S FREEZING. I'VE NEVER BEEN SO COLD IN ALL MY LIFE!

Serviced and bombed up, the Lancs took off for Alten Fiord.

HERE WE GO, LADS. THE GERMANS WON'T BE EXPECTING US FROM THIS DIRECTION.

CONTINUED ON BACK PAGE

The Lancs roared into the attack and immediately the Tirpitz poured out a screen of smoke.

CONTINUED FROM FRONT PAGE

SOUND THE ALARM, HERR LIEUTENANT. THE RADAR HAS PICKED UP ENEMY AIRCRAFT HEADING STRAIGHT FOR THE TIRPITZ.

BOMB GONE, SKIPPER, BUT THE OTHER LADS WON'T HAVE A MARK TO AIM AT.

Back in Britain, the crews learned that they had scored a direct hit.

This was confirmed by a Norwegian patriot who radioed to Britain that the Tirpitz had limped into Tromso Fiord.

WITH THE AIRCRAFT LIGHTENED AND EXTRA FUEL TANKS IN THE FUSELAGE, THE LANCS CAN REACH THE TIRPITZ FROM LOSSIEMOUTH, IN SCOTLAND.

One night, in November 1944, the famous Dam Busters, 617 Squadron, set out to finish the job.

THREE O' CLOCK IN THE MORNING! WHAT A TIME TO START A RAID!

UP WE GO. HERE'S WHERE THE GERRY FIGHTERS GET THEIR RADAR WARNING. LOOK OUT, GUNNERS!

BOMB GONE!

YIPPEE! WE WON'T HAVE TO COME BACK HERE AGAIN.

THREE HITS IN A ROW.

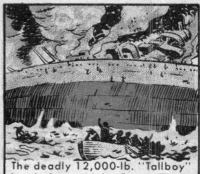

The deadly 12,000-lb. "Tallboy" bombs battered the German giant and finally she keeled over and turned turtle. In two raids, the R.A.F. had removed Germany's greatest menace to merchant shipping.

SEE PAGE 174 for the next colour cover story.

PRINTED AND PUBLISHED IN GREAT BRITAIN BY D. C. THOMSON & CO., LTD. AND JOHN LENG & CO., LTD., 12 FETTER LANE, FLEET STREET, LONDON, E.C.4. REGISTERED FOR TRANSMISSION BY CANADIAN MAGAZINE POST. © D. C. THOMSON & CO., LTD., 1961.

Maverick Carson was the favourite butt of the town's bullies—anyone could push him around. Then he joined the Pony Express!

TALES of the PONY EXPRESS

So young "Maverick" Carson took the oath and joined the Pony Express. The active, open-air life and plenty of good food made a new man of him.

The call for help that spelt danger!

"*A club talks the kind of language Blackie understands.*"

Tom Hughes vowed vengeance—and he took a terrible toll of the Japs who wiped out his mortar platoon!

The FORGOTTEN FOURTEENTH

THE massed Jap forces, wearing hideous masks and screaming their battle cries, charged the British front line. It was February, 1944, and the Japanese were launching a ferocious attack against the British Fifteenth Corps of the British Fourteenth Army, in Burma. Soon, Divisional Headquarters of the British Seventh Division were under heavy fire.

WE'RE ABOUT AT THE END OF OUR AMMUNITION, SIR.

WE SHALL HAVE TO PULL OUT AND RETIRE TO THE CORPS ADMINSTRATION AREA.

COME ON, HUGHES—HURRY!

CLARKE'S HIT, SIR, BUT I'LL BRING HIM ALONG. WE'RE THE ONLY SURVIVORS.

Other troops joined the two officers.

KEEP YOUR EYES SKINNED FOR JAPS, THEY COULD HAVE CUT OUR LINE OF RETREAT.

WE'VE BEEN AMBUSHED—TAKE COVER!

BANZAI!

NO YOU DON'T, MATEY!

Tom Hughes survived the Jap ambush, and reached 15th Corps Headquarters.

HE'S DEAD, CHUM, BETTER LEAVE HIM HERE.

POOR OLD NOBBY. THAT MAKES ME THE ONLY ONE LEFT OF OUR MORTAR PLATOON—AND WE LOST ALL THE MORTARS TOO!

" Plenty of bombs—but no mortars!"

MORTARMAN TOM HUGHES, REPORTING FOR DUTY, SIR.

CAN'T HELP IT, SOLDIER, WE'VE GOT NO MORTARS. YOU'LL HAVE TO FIGHT AS A RIFLE-AND-BAYONET MAN INSTEAD.

GET THESE TRENCHES DUG DEEPER.

LOOKS LIKE BEING CLOSE QUARTER STUFF, EH, HUGHES?

YES, BUT WE'LL HOLD THE JAPS OFF, OKAY—AS LONG AS OUR FOOD AND AMMO LAST OUT.

THEY WILL. WE'RE GOING TO BE SUPPLIED BY PARACHUTE—YOU KNOW, DROP THE STUFF FROM AEROPLANES.

Encouraged by their early success, the Japs launched one attack after another at the defenders of the 15th Corps Admin. Box.

WELL DONE, LADS. HANG ON—DON'T YIELD AN INCH. WE'VE GOT THEM ON THE RUN AGAIN!

KEEP YOUR EYES OPEN, LADS. THERE'LL BE MORE HAND-TO-HAND FIGHTING.

WE REALLY NEED MORTARS, SIR, TO BREAK UP THESE ATTACKS EARLY ON.

CHEER UP, TOM, MAYBE THEY'LL DROP US A FEW MORTARS FROM THE AIR.

Later.

HERE THEY COME! BOY—JUST LOOK AT ALL THAT STUFF COMING DOWN.

WE CAN SURE USE IT.

THERE'S ONE OF THE PLANES GOING DOWN, POOR BLIGHTER.

YES, AND SOME OF OUR CONTAINERS ARE DRIFTING OVER TO THE JAP POSITIONS.

ALL MORTARMEN THIS WAY, AT THE DOUBLE!

YIPEE! THEY MUST HAVE SOME MORTARS AFTER ALL!

THAT'S ALL THE CONTAINERS EMPTIED, SIR—AND WE'VE GOT PLENTY OF BOMBS BUT NO MORTARS!

BLAST OUR ROTTEN LUCK! THE MORTARS MUST HAVE DRIFTED INTO THE JAP LINES—OR ELSE THEY WERE ON THE PLANE THAT WAS SHOT DOWN.

WE'RE SUNK, LADS. THE MORTARS HAVE GONE ASTRAY, AND THE JAPS ARE MASSING FOR ANOTHER ATTACK. YOU'D BETTER GET BACK TO YOUR TRENCHES.

MAYBE HE'S SUNK—BUT I'M NOT!

WAIT A MINUTE, BLOKES, GIVE ME A HAND. I'VE AN IDEA!

The bamboo tubes that won a battle.

THAT'S THE IDEA—CUT DOWN THE THICK STEMS OF BAMBOO.

DIG THERE, CHUM, ABOUT THREE FEET WILL DO. MAKE THE HOLE JUST WIDE ENOUGH TO TAKE A BIG BAMBOO SECTION.

PHEW! IT'S A TIGHT FIT, CHUM—BUT THAT'S ALL TO THE GOOD.

THIS BAYONET WILL STICK UP IN THE BOTTOM OF THE INNER BAMBOO TUBE AND SERVE AS A FIRING PIN.

IT'S A CUTE IDEA, TOM. I JUST HOPE IT WORKS!

THAT OUGHT TO BE ABOUT THE RIGHT ANGLE. RAM THE EARTH ROUND IT REAL TIGHT!

HERE COME THE JAPS—HUNDREDS OF THEM!

GRAB SOME BOMBS, YOU LADS, AND GET READY TO FIRE.

I DON'T KNOW HOW MANY ROUNDS THESE THINGS WILL STAND—BUT FIRE THREE ROUNDS THEN INSPECT YOUR GUN!

RIGHT-O, TOM, AND THE BEST OF LUCK TO ALL OF US.

THEY WORK! THE DEAR OLD CANNONS ARE JUST THE JOB!

I ONLY HOPE THE BAMBOO BARRELS STAND UP FOR THREE ROUNDS.

The unexpected mortar support surprised the front line troops—but even more surprised were the Japs!

OUR MORTARS HAVE OPENED FIRE. WOW—LOOK AT THE WAY THEY'RE PLASTERING THE JAPS!

MORTARS? BUT IT'S IMPOSSIBLE—WE DON'T HAVE ANY MORTARS.

ATTACK! NO RETREAT—YOU MUST ATTACK!

YOU'VE JUST ABOUT SAVED THE DAY, HUGHES, WITH THESE BAMBOO MORTARS OF YOURS. WE'LL HAVE SOME REAL ONES DELIVERED BEFORE THE NEXT JAP ATTACK.

IT WAS A MAGNIFICENT IDEA, HUGHES. I SEE YOU MANNED YOUR MORTARS UNTIL THEY COULDN'T FIRE ANOTHER ROUND. WELL DONE.

Later.

NOW WE'LL REALLY SHAKE THE JAPS IF THEY ATTACK AGAIN.

Morgyn the Mighty's life is saved — thanks to an animal ally!

SEVEN TRAILS TO MORGYN THE MIGHTY

When six hunters and their Zulu tracker came to shoot big game in the Ompopo valley in Africa, they found that Morgyn the Mighty, the strongest man in the world, had driven most of the animals out of the valley to save their lives. In a fury the seven men decided to hunt Morgyn instead. But the strong man proved a difficult prey and now only two of the hunters were left in the valley. One day Morgyn went swimming . . .

MORGYN! THIS IS AMAZING. WE HAVE HUNTED HIM FOR SO LONG AND NOW I COME UPON HIM BY ACCIDENT. I MUST NOT WASTE MY CHANCE!

GENTLY DOES IT! SOON THE MAN WHO SPOILED OUR SPORT WILL BE DEAD!

But 'Morgyn had an unknown ally . . .

WH-WHAT? STUPID BABOON! IT HAS PUT MY AIM OFF!

I'LL SWIM UPSTREAM AND DOUBLE BACK ON WHOEVER FIRED THAT SHOT.

I'LL SOON FIND THE CULPRIT.

DON'T THINK YOU CAN ESCAPE FROM ME.

Later — DO NOT THINK YOU'VE KILLED ME, VON BERG! I'M VERY MUCH ALIVE BUT YOU WON'T BE FOR LONG!

WH-WHAT? I'M GETTING OUT OF HERE!

I MUST HAVE KILLED HIM AFTER ALL, DESPITE THAT BABOON.

" Get me out of this or I'm doomed!"

CONTINUED ON PAGE 169 Morgyn finds himself at the mercy of the only remaining hunter!

The spine-chilling story of the runner who shattered the track record—yet was convinced he was second!

THE PHANTOM IN LANE FOUR

ALAN BRADFIELD'S reputation was already very high. He was listed up among the world-class sprinters. Two or three runs of 9.4 for the 100 yards and several below 21 seconds for the 220 had seen to that.

Now, for the first time in I don't know how many years, we watched a British runner actually set a world record in a sprint race. It was at a special meeting on our own Elmfield Harriers ground. My name's Albert Carson, by the way.

The cinder track was new, iron-hard, like the tracks in California, and with the bends less sharp than, for example, the White City track down in London. The afternoon was warm, dry and windless, perfect conditions for sprinting—and Bradfield took full advantage of them!

In this 220 yards race, he had the three other leading British sprinters against him, men who were themselves capable of somewhere around 21 seconds for the distance, men who had occasionally beaten him in other races. This time, he left them standing.

From the gun, we knew it was going to be a terrific run. Bradfield got away well, which he didn't always do.

Within ten yards his famous pick-up had come into operation. Being in the second lane, he had the incentive of men outside him to pull him along, and he went so fast you couldn't follow his movement in a steady sweep of vision. You had to keep on jerking your head round so as to catch up with him.

Coming into the long home straight, he was already two yards up on his nearest rival. Absolutely steady he ran, so that you would have sworn his legs were running away with him.

Everything must have gone right. He had that surge of speed which you sometimes see at the end of a hundred yards dash, when a man suddenly gets into a kind of overdrive which seems to pull him away from his competitors as if they'd slowed down to a walk.

Bradfield was keeping this surge going with power and resolution. Unfaltering, poised and purposeful, he swept over the last twenty yards of red cinders and hit the tape four yards in the lead.

Instantly, I pressed the lever of my own stop watch where I stood high up in the stand. When I looked, the watch read 20.5 seconds !

A new world record had just been

A COACH CARSON STORY

introduced for the furlong run round a bend. So far, an American held the record with a time of 20.6. Had Bradfield beaten that time, or had I made an error myself ?

Then a tremendous shout went up from the crowd. The three official timekeepers down at the track had evidently recorded the same time on their watches. It came over the loudspeakers—

"First, Bradfield, in a time of 20.5 seconds, which is a new world, United Kingdom All-Comers, United Kingdom National, and A.A.A. National record !"

Everybody went wild ! Down on the track, Alan Bradfield was submerged under a wave of men congratulating him.

It turned out later, that two watches had shown 20.5 seconds, and the other, 20.4.

The second man had returned 20.9, and two others 21 seconds dead. It must have been by far the fastest all-round race that Britain had ever seen, and Bradfield had done it on his own home track in front of his own home crowd.

They must have heard the noise twenty miles away, at Southgate, the place where our chief rivals, Southgate Harriers, had their track.

As the official coach to Elmfield Harriers, I took some small part of the credit for the record myself. I must confess, though, that for some time now, Alan Bradfield had got beyond the point where I could teach him anything.

"Finest sprinter Britain's ever produced," someone near me in the crowd said.

"At last we've got a man who can even show the American sprinters something !" came a second comment. "We've waited for it long enough."

Then a thin but strong voice introduced a most unexpected counter-opinion.

"The trouble with you chaps," the voice said, "is that you either have short memories, or you're too young to have any memories at all !"

"Huh ?"

The men in the crowd turned round to face the owner of the voice. I recognised old Barty Timmins. A man of seventy-five, he'd been a fine distance runner in his time.

"Are you trying to say that wasn't a great effort ?" one of the men asked.

Barty Timmins shook his head.

"It was a fine run, by a fine sprinter. But what I'm saying is that Alan Bradfield isn't the first world-class sprinter we've had in this country by any means.

"He isn't the first Britisher to hold a world sprint record, and he isn't the first

sprinter to beat the Yanks!"

As I moved over towards Barty, I guessed what he was going to say. But the men standing round about him were all quite young, and his remarks puzzled them.

"All right, tell us, old 'un," one of them invited good-naturedly. "Which British sprinter has ever been as good as Bradfield?"

"Teddy Pearmain, of course," the old man snapped. "And he wasn't just as good as Bradfield, he was better!"

The declaration caused laughter. Barty's eyes gleamed frostily.

"I tell you he was. I saw him run many a time. In 1911 I saw him set a mark of 21.2 for the 220 on the Southgate County cricket ground.

"At the time, that was a world record—and for nearly half a century it stood as a British record. It's only within the last two or three years that our young sparks have been able to get anywhere near it!"

PAST v. PRESENT

WELL, you know how it is. The achievements of one generation mean nothing to the succeeding generation.

All these men must have heard of Teddy Pearmain, but the knowledge they had of him was slight. They'd never seen him run, as they'd seen Bradfield.

Indeed, Pearmain hadn't done much running after setting his record. There'd been a tragedy on the Southgate cricket ground, when Pearmain died on the track.

The younger men moved away. I approached Barty.

"Do you really think Pearmain was better than Bradfield?" I asked him.

The faded grey eyes looked at me.

"I do, Albert."

"But consider the times, Barty," I objected. "We've just seen Bradfield return 20.5, whereas Pearmain's best effort was 21.2."

"And consider the sort of tracks both men ran on," Barty replied. "That track down there is as hard as concrete, perfect for sprinting. Pearmain set his record on a grass surface which was good and springy, and not specially designed for running.

"Bradfield had first-class

opposition to spur him on. Teddy Pearmain didn't. He made his effort entirely on his own, without being able to hoist himself up on other men's shoulders!"

Well, of course, I had to concede those points. For a little while, Barty Timmins went on reminiscing about Pearmain and other great names of the days before the First World War. But the reminiscing really didn't get us anywhere.

There's always the temptation to compare the runners of yesterday with the runners of today, and how can you, since you can't put them in an arena against each other?

Yet it turned out that a comparison of a sort was possible. Fifty years had elapsed since Pearmain set his record. Southgate Harriers decided to hold a Jubilee Meeting to celebrate the event.

Instead of having the meeting on their own track, they decided to let it take place on the County cricket ground. On that grass surface Pearmain had returned 9.7 for the hundred, and 21.2 for the two-twenty.

Southgate Harriers now challenged Bradfield and the other leading British sprinters to see if they could better those times under the same conditions!

INTO THE PAST

WELL, the thing fairly caught the public imagination. The Southgate officials decided to do the job in style and turned out in dress appropriate to the year 1911.

Instead of the grass track being marked out with chalk lines, as it would be nowadays, they adopted the old method of marking lanes with tapes running through iron pegs at a height of about a foot from the ground.

A lot of other period touches were introduced. Someone drove to the ground in a coach, and someone else filled up a brake with spectators all in period costume.

It gave an odd feeling to those people, like myself, who retained a recollection of those days before the First World War, even if the recollection was only a dim one. We felt that we had been mysteriously transported back in time.

Even the runners, all young men, some of them not remem-

bering very much even about the Second World War, were affected. Uneasily they trotted around as the military band played tunes appropriate to those days.

It suddenly seemed to strike them that they were pitting themselves against a real person, and not just a name. Teddy Pearmain had been dead these fifty years, and it was here that he died, but his influence still seemed to brood over this stretch of green turf and the people who encircled it.

A photograph of him setting his world record had been stuck up on a table, and all his silver cups and medals arranged around it.

We could feel the modern world receding away from us, and the old days thickening like the clouds that were starting to cover the evening sky.

There was no electronic public address system, of course. Announcements were bellowed through a megaphone. A full programme of events had been arranged, but only two had real interest for the crowd—the hundred yards and the furlong.

"Will you all rise and observe a two minutes' silence in memory of E. Pearmain, world record sprinter and member of Southgate Harriers!" the voice boomed through the megaphone.

There was a rustling as people rose to their feet. Out on the grass, athletes came to attention.

Then there followed a period of silence which was so intense that it almost shrieked. I could feel my heart pounding against my ribs. Near me, a woman looked so pale I thought she was going to faint.

We were conscious of something. Standing and staring at that photograph, we felt the skin prickling at the backs of

our necks. Had we started something we were going to be sorry for?

The starter's gun, as he fired a practice shot, broke the silence. It also made the crowd jump almost out of their skins.

The sky was growing darker. I thought I saw lightning flickering in the distance. They'd better get through this meeting quickly, I thought, otherwise we would collect a soaking.

A half-mile came first, then a high hurdles race—run with the old-fashioned wooden barriers, and under the old rules whereby if you knocked over three you were disqualified—then came the hundred yards.

TERRIBLE TENSION

I COULDN'T bear the tension and left the stand to go out on to the grass middle. The Southgate officials knew me and didn't object.

At the end of the tape-marked track, six sprinters were busy digging holes. It was something I don't suppose any of them had ever done before. They'd never used any starting device except blocks.

The air was breathlessly hot, and the light was growing worse, as they got down to their holes. From where I was standing, none of them looked easy, which accounted for the two false starts.

Then they were away! Bradfield got a poor start, as so often with him. Even from my angle I could see that he was at least a yard down at twenty.

He recovered fast, developing his pick-up, and really letting fly. At sixty yards he was showing fractionally in front, and starting to go away.

A gust of wind howled down that track, as if someone had opened a giant door. Dust rose in clouds, obscuring the scene.

Coming out of absolute stillness, the gust startled us. It moaned and keened in our ears. My eyes watered where the dust stung them.

Bradfield was through the tape, winning by a yard. At the same time the wind died away, leaving the air absolutely calm once more. People looked at each other, a little scared.

"Storm coming," they mumbled. "I reckon it'll blow up pretty soon."

Possibly Alan Bradfield had been put off by the unexpected atmospheric disturbance, though the gust of wind had seemed to be blowing down the track.

At any rate, his time for the hundred was given as 9.8 seconds. Instead of beating Teddy Pearmain's record, he hadn't even been able to match it!

"What's up, Alan?" I asked him. "Not feeling so good?"

He shook his head.

"I don't know, Albert. I feel fine physically, as good as I did when I set that world record, but there's something here that's sort of cramping my style.

"Can't make it out. Maybe I've been put off by these tapes and the hole-digging and the 1911 pageant."

"Never mind, you'll do better in the furlong," I assured him.

With the new world record holder having failed to match the old world record holder in the short sprint, the crowd's interest in the furlong was heightened. You could feel tension building up like an electric charge.

Was Bradfield going to do it this time? Or would Teddy Pearmain's ground record in the longer sprint still remain intact. Would the old-timer prove to have been better than the rising generation?

Bradfield himself was looking stern and resolute. He didn't like the thought of his earlier failure. I knew that this time he'd pull all the stops out.

THE PHANTOM

IN gloom so dark that it was more like the

approach of night, the same six invited sprinters dug their holes in the turf of the cricket pitch. Bradfield was in lane three.

Bradfield's start was a beauty! He came out of those holes like a shell driven from the barrel of a gun.

We strained our eyes to watch those six figures sweeping round the bend towards the long home straight.

Five rivals? My blood suddenly froze. Something had happened to my vision. The gloom was causing it to play tricks. I could have sworn there were six other figures on that track in addition to our new world record holder!

The wind came blasting again with a savage, elemental force.

In face of the screaming, tearing noise, the shouts of the crowd grew thin and died away, but Bradfield was still going like a runaway train.

This time, surely, he must have achieved what he set out to do. Behind him the others were faltering.

Except for one man, who was coming up fast. Coming up fast on Alan Bradfield at the end of a killing race when he was running at a speed that no one in the world could match!

The tape was broken. That wind died away. A few big drops of rain started to fall. In a voice of great excitement, the announcer called through his megaphone.

"Result of the 220 yards. First, Bradfield, time, 21.0 seconds!"

The crowd erupted in a tremendous yell. So the old-timer had been beaten by the modern generation. For fifty years Teddy Pearmain had held the ground record here to his credit. Now the name of Alan Bradfield would take over.

I rushed across to congratulate our Elmfield star.

"Well done, Alan! That was a great run."

Bradfield looked at me. He was breathing deeply, his face white and worried.

"Albert, did you notice anything odd about that race?"

"Er, no, not really, just that gust of wind. Why?"

"You know the judges gave me first?" he said.

I nodded.

"And you know when you're first, and you go through the tape, you feel the tension of the worsted as it snaps under your thrust?"

"Yes," I agreed.

Bradfield's eyes were dark with worry.

"When I crossed the line, Albert, I didn't feel any tension in the worsted. Someone had snapped it just before me."

His voice rose until it cracked.

"I didn't win that race. I didn't break Teddy Pearmain's record. I think he came back to break it himself! He was the phantom in lane four!"

SPECIAL COMPLETE STORY. The Red MacGregor and his friends are being hunted by the English Redcoats. Why then do they help cut timber to build English ships?

THE RED MACGREGOR

The Red MacGregor, the most famous of that outlawed clan, and his comrades, Englishman Hal o' the Heath and Frenchman Laughing John, were constantly on the run in the Scottish Highlands. The Redcoats were determined to capture them and, using ferocious dogs, they tracked the trio for days.

"The Redcoat fools expect the dogs to cross the flame!"

The three friends moved on to a quiet stream and settled down to catch some fish.

"That will teach you never to lay a hand on me again."

" We've killed them! We'll go down in history for this."

A cricket crackpot goes on the warpath. He means to stop Joe bowling for England— with a gun!

IS IT CRICKET?

There was great excitement during the Second Test Match at Trent Bridge in Nottingham. The Australians' 1961 tour of England had started with a resounding victory for Australia in the First Test. But now England had a secret weapon— 18-year-old Joe Doone, a bowling wizard, who had never played cricket in his life. England were all out in their first innings for 270 runs, and Joe's high, drooping wrong 'un had taken the first of the Australians' wickets.

THAT WAS A QUEER BALL DOONE GOT YOU OUT WITH, COBBER.

I'VE NEVER SEEN SUCH A FLUKE.

WHAT KIND OF BOWLING IS THIS? SO IT WASN'T A FLUKE AFTER ALL!

The next batsman thought he knew how to deal with a wrong 'un.

THIS WILL FOOL HIM!

HOWZATT?

At the end of the innings, Joe walked off to a tremendous ovation. Australia were all out for 118, and Joe had taken eight wickets for only 12 runs.

But one spectator was not pleased—Mr O. D. Bleakes, a cricket crackpot.

DOONE'S BOWLING IS NOT CRICKET! I MUST STOP HIM PLAYING. HE IS RUINING THE GAME!

Next day, before the start of play.

AND SO I ASK YOU, MY FRIENDS, IN THE NAME OF CRICKET, TO BOYCOTT THIS MATCH AND ALL OTHER MATCHES IN WHICH JOE DOONE BOWLS. HE IS MAKING A MOCKERY OF THE GREAT AND NOBLE GAME OF CRICKET.

ARE YOU AN AUSSIE, MATE?

A JOKER LIKE YOU SHOULD BE ON THE STAGE!

"Cricket must be saved from this menace."

SO THEY WILL NOT LISTEN! THEN THERE IS ONLY ONE THING TO DO!

Mr Bleake hurried home and took an old revolver from a drawer.

I MUST SHOOT JOE DOONE! CRICKET MUST BE SAVED FROM THIS MENACE!

The Australians followed on 152 runs behind England.

I'VE GOT THE ANSWER THIS TIME—I THINK!

IT WORKED!

THIS IS A BIT OF A PROBLEM. I WONDER HOW I CAN GET HIM OUT?

TRY THAT ONE, MATE!

At lunch, the Aussies had scored 52 for six wickets, and Joe had taken five of them. He was grabbed by newspaper photographers as he left the field.

THE BOYS WOULD LIKE SOME PHOTOS OF YOU, JOE. WOULD YOU COME OVER TO THE SIDE OF THE PAVILION?

SURE, TED.

HERE IS MY CHANCE.

OH-H-H!

A bullet for the bowler.

Every boy whose name appears on this page gets a prize!

POST BAG PARADE

Do-It-Yourself Ref

A Spanish referee awarded a penalty and then three times disallowed a goal because the goalie moved. The chap who had taken the penalties was so annoyed that he shouted to the referee—"Take it yourself!" The referee did so, scored and awarded a goal.

—A Postal Order to Stuart Pike, 9 Solent Road, East Wattering, Sussex, near Chichester.

★ ★ ★ ★

Crumbs!

The world's biggest cake, more than ten feet long, five feet wide and nine feet high, has been made by bakers working from architects' drawings. Weighing more than two tons, covered with marzipan and icing, it is expected to be the centrepiece at the opening of the British Industries Fair.

—A Postal Order to Roy Lavery, 47 Clonduff Drive, Castlereagh Road, Belfast, 6, N. Ireland.

This Is *YOUR* Page!

A ten-shilling Postal Order is presented to the writer of every letter on this page. A special prize —a pair of ROLLER SKATES or a No. 3 MECCANO SET—also goes to the boys who send in the two star letters of the week.

Send YOUR entry to—
POST BAG PARADE,
"THE VICTOR,"
12 FETTER LANE,
FLEET STREET,
LONDON, E.C.4.

When you write to the Editor, please mention your age and the two stories you like best in "The Victor."

Timid Bulls

At an experimental bull-fight at Tilburg, Holland, the bulls just wouldn't fight. In front of some 7000 spectators the bulls, which were imported from Spain, started to eat the grass in the bull ring. The matadors jumped about in front of the bulls in an attempt to make them fight, but they failed.

—Postal Order to Robert G. Smith, 84 Victoria Road, Aston, Birmingham 6.

★ ★ ★ ★

Cure For Blindness

Eighty - year - old Vittoria Starnone was blind and had been for many years. One day he slipped on the tiles of the kitchen floor in his house in Italy, bumped his head rather hard and was knocked out.

When his son arrived at his house and found Vittoria lying unconscious on the floor he slapped his father's face to try to bring him round again.

He succeeded. But he was absolutely astounded when his father told him he was able to see. The fall had cured his blindness.

—A Postal Order to Anthony Brown, Brockagh, Eglinton, Co. Derry, N. Ireland.

★ ★ ★ ★

Long Hair

A normal man has about 25,000 hairs on his face, and each of them grows roughly one-hundredth of an inch every 24 hours—so that altogether a clean-shaven man removes 250 inches (or nearly 21 feet) of hair every time he shaves.

—A Postal Order to E. Paul, 2 Croxted Close, West Dulwich, London, S.E.21.

★ ★ ★ ★

The Real Thing

Six greyhounds dashed out of the traps and began chasing the mechanical hare at Great Yarmouth Stadium. Then they stopped, turned, and went after something much more interesting — a rabbit.

It had got into the stadium from the nearby marshes and fields. The event was officially declared "no race."

—Postal Order to Tony Haresnape, 2 Trowels Lane, Derby.

★ ★ ★ ★

Ice-Holes

Experiments are being carried out by the American Air Force of dropping ice particles from specially constructed aeroplanes on to a layer of cloud. By using only 12 pounds of ice particles, a hole with a diameter of about three miles was made in a layer of cloud, through which the earth's surface was clearly visible.

—A Postal Order to William Walker, 41 Irvine Road, New-milns, Ayrshire.

★ ★ ★ ★

Top Score

The highest number of operations reported on one patient is the 410 undergone by the South African soldier, Lionel De Witt. He received them in nine years, following extensive injuries from a land mine at the battle of El Alamein.

—A Postal Order to Fraser Macdonald, 16 Freegrove Road, Holloway, London, N.7.

★ ★ ★ ★

Pole Squatter

William Howard, of Santa Monica, California, had a cast-iron alibi when police questioned him about a robbery of which he was suspected. At the time of the robbery Howard was sitting on top of a 65-foot flagpole for a publicity stunt.

—A Postal Order to Paul Downes, 244 Lodge Causeway, Fishponds, Bristol.

★ ★ ★ ★

The Emden

I was very interested in the front-page story, "The end of the Emden," in the "The Victor," because my father has the pistol belonging to the captain of the Emden, Captain von Muller.

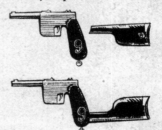

He got it from my grandfather, who got it from a captain in the Royal Navy.

Captain von Muller's pistol can be made into a rifle by clipping the wooden holster on the end of the butt as shown in the illustration above. On the side of the butt of the pistol, which is a German Mauser, is a large figure 9.

—Postal Order to John Wilson, Filleigh Mill House, Filleigh, nr. Barnstaple, North Devon.

★ *Star Letters* ★

If you opened the front door of a house in Leinster Terrace, London, you'd find yourself outside again! The house isn't a house at all; it is merely a wall painted to look like one. It is part of a terrace of tall houses known as Leinster Garden Mansions, behind which is a cutting of the Metropolitan Railway. The "dummy house" was built to hide the railway.

—A Postal Order and a Special Prize to Thomas McHugh, 11 Bowden Park, Westwood, East Kilbride, Glasgow.

★ ★ ★ ★

During World War Two, H.M. Submarine Umbra, on patrol in the Mediterranean, sighted an enemy ammunition ship. She attacked the ship with torpedoes and hit her. The ship blew up just as an escorting plane passed over her and the blast blew the plane out of the sky as well.

—A Postal Order and a Special Prize to Christopher Gough, 6 Windsor Drive, Marple, Cheshire.

161

Braddock is ready, the Big Bomb is in the bomb bay, everything is set for the vital raid—
but the target has disappeared!

I FLEW WITH BRADDOCK

LOOK, GEORGE, THAT WAS A MASTER LANDING.

YES, BRADDOCK STYLE. I WONDER WHO THE PILOT IS?

HEY, I'VE SEEN HIM BEFORE. THAT'S GROUP CAPTAIN RODERICK AMBERLEY. I WAS ON THE SAME STATION AS HIM ONCE. HE'S THE BLOKE WHO BOMBED BERLIN IN DAYLIGHT.

Sergeant Matt Braddock, V.C., was the greatest pilot of the last war. This is the story of the famous book about him, written by George Bourne, his navigator. Braddock was to make a special mission to drop a big, new bomb, designed by Mr Smith, a brilliant scientist, on the Degen, Germany's new aircraft-carrier. The Degen was a deadly threat to British shipping. A new commanding officer was due to arrive at Barminster R.A.F. Station, which had previously been badly run. Now Bourne and Tom Tanner, the bomb-aimer of F Fox, Braddock's Lancaster, watched a Mosquito land.

HOW ARE YOU, TANNER? AND YOU, SERGEANT? YOU'VE DONE A LOT OF FIGHTING JUDGING BY THOSE MEDALS.

I'M SERGEANT BRADDOCK'S NAVIGATOR, SIR.

I'M FLYING OFFICER PROUT, SIR, THE ACTING ADJUTANT.

I'M AMBERLEY. I'M TAKING OVER COMMAND HERE. SHOW ME THE KITCHENS.

FANCY HIM REMEMBERING ME.

COME ON, TOM. LET'S WATCH THIS. I'VE AN IDEA IT'S GOING TO BE WORTH SEEING!

Amberley hit the cookhouse like a whirlwind . . .

PUT OUT THAT CIGARETTE!

THIS SOUP IS DREADFUL!

GET THESE CLEANED. THIS PLACE IS FILTHY! GET THE FLOORS WASHED!

WHAT CRIMINAL LEFT THAT THERE?

. . . then continued his inspection of the station.

LOOK, GEORGE, THEY'RE ACTUALLY WORKING IN THERE. IT'S THE FIRST TIME FOR AGES.

COME ON, LET'S SEE SOME MORE FUN.

LEFT, RIGHT, LEFT, RIGHT. PICK 'EM UP THERE!

HALT! ARE YOU PLAYING TIN SOLDIERS, FLIGHT SERGEANT?

IT'S CUSTOMARY TO MARCH THE MEN TO AND FROM WORK, SIR!

THEY'RE HERE TO KEEP AEROPLANES FLYING, NOT TO IMITATE THE HOME GUARD. I CAN FIND MORE WORK FOR MY FLIGHT SERGEANTS. DISMISS THE MEN.

The hidden menace in the mist!

WHERE DOES THAT DOOR LEAD TO?

THE MAP STORE, SIR!

SHUT THE DOOR, CAN'T YOU? THERE'S A DRAUGHT.

WHAT ARE YOU DOING IN HERE, BRADDOCK?

I'M TRYING TO WORK OUT WHERE TO LOOK FOR THE DEGEN, IT'S GONE FROM KIEL, AND OUR RECONNAISSANCE PLANES HAVEN'T BEEN ABLE TO FIND IT BECAUSE OF POOR VISIBILITY.

HAVE YOU COME TO ANY CONCLUSIONS ABOUT IT?

I DON'T THINK IT HAS PASSED THROUGH THE CANAL. I RECKON IT MUST BE SLINKING UP THE GREAT BELT TOWARDS THE KATTEGAT.

I'VE GOT A MOSQUITO OUTSIDE. LET'S GO AND LOOK FOR OURSELVES.

WHAT A MAN AMBERLEY IS, TOM. HE'S ONLY BEEN HERE HALF AN HOUR AND THE WHOLE STATION'S CHANGED —AND THERE HE GOES ON AN OPERATIONAL FLIGHT BEFORE HE'S EVEN BEEN TO HIS OFFICE!

Later.

ACK-ACK, BRADDOCK.

YES, WE'RE GETTING NEARER THE GREAT BELT NOW.

IT'S PRETTY HOPELESS, BRADDOCK. WE'VE BEEN SEARCHING FOR HOURS, NOW, AND NOT A SIGN OF THE DEGEN.

IT'S SOMEWHERE AHEAD.

THAT'S JUST A GUESS.

NO IT ISN'T. LOOK AT ALL THAT RUBBISH. A BIG SHIP'S GONE. THIS WAY.

THERE IT IS!

WE'VE FOUND IT! LET'S GET HOME!

PITY WE DIDN'T HAVE ANY BOMBS WITH US.

THEY'D ONLY DO SUPERFICIAL DAMAGE. WE NEED THE BIG BOMB TO SINK IT. I'LL WIRELESS BACK TO BASE AND HAVE THE LADS STAND BY FOR IMMEDIATE TAKE-OFF.

"Bomb doors open!"

That evening, F Fox took off on one of the most vital missions of the war.

PILOT TO CREW. KEEP YOUR EYES SKINNED. THE DEGEN CAN'T BE FAR AWAY.

NAVIGATOR TO PILOT. WE'RE ON THE EDGE OF THE SEARCH AREA NOW.

DROP FLARES!

WE'VE FOUND IT! OVER TO YOU, BOMB-AIMER. BOMB DOORS OPEN!

LEFT, LEFT, STEADY—

HOW IS HE, NICKER? I'LL GIVE YOU A HAND.

HE'S ONLY STUNNED. I THINK THE NOSE CAP OF A SHELL HIT US. I'LL TAKE TOM BACK TO MY COMPARTMENT.

TOM! WHAT'S HAPPENED TO HIM? GO AND SEE, HAM.

STEADY DOES IT!

HE'LL BE ALL RIGHT, HAM. IT'S JUST A SCALP WOUND.

RIGHT, I'LL REPORT TO BRAD.

TOM WILL BE ALL RIGHT, BUT WE'VE HAD IT. THE NOSE IS WRECKED AND THE BOMB SIGHT WITH IT. WE'LL HAVE TO TAKE THE BOMB BACK.

NO, TAKE OVER THE CONTROLS. I'LL DROP THE BOMB!

BUT THE SIGHT'S WRECKED!

I HEARD. YOU DO THE DRIVING, I'LL GET DOWN TO THE BOMB-AIMER'S COMPARTMENT.

The deadly eyes of Sergeant Braddock!

IT'S NOT TOO BAD. AT LEAST THE BOMB RELEASE GEAR LOOKS ALL RIGHT.

STEADY NOW, HAM, YOU'RE WANDERING A BIT. KEEP DEAD STEADY. NOW. COMING UP. NOW!

BOMB GONE!

WE GOT IT! WE GOT IT! IT'S SPLIT IN TWO!

A few hours later, F Fox landed at Craxby and was met by an enthusiastic reception committee.

THEN SEND THE SIGNAL, NICKER, SEND THEM "DENTED".

"Dented" was the pre-arranged signal that the mission had been successful.

LOOK AT MR SMITH, DO YOU THINK HE'S PLEASED ABOUT SOMETHING?

TOUGH LUCK ON TANNER THAT HE SHOULD BE KNOCKED OUT AFTER HIS SPLENDID WORK.

NOT A CHEEP OUT OF YOU, HAM. I DON'T WANT A LOT OF FUSS.

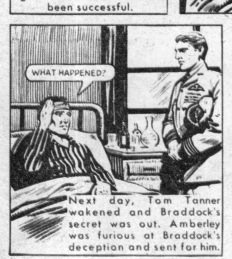

WHAT HAPPENED?

Next day, Tom Tanner wakened and Braddock's secret was out. Amberley was furious at Braddock's deception and sent for him.

YOU HAD NO BUSINESS TO SUPPRESS THAT GEN, BRADDOCK. WE MUST KNOW HOW THINGS ARE DONE. I DON'T CARE WHETHER YOU WANTED A FUSS OR NOT. WHEN YOU RETURN FROM A MISSION, IT IS YOUR DUTY TO PROVIDE THE INTELLIGENCE OFFICERS WITH A FULL REPORT. REGARD YOURSELF AS SEVERELY REPRIMANDED!

YES, SIR.

BUT IT WAS A FIRST CLASS SHOW, SERGEANT BRADDOCK —A FIRST CLASS SHOW!

THE END

Are the Rovers' championship hopes doomed? They take the field in their vital league decider one man short—and that man is Gorgeous Gus!

GORGEOUS GUS

The Earl of Boote, known as Gorgeous Gus, was the owner of Redburn Rovers and played centre-forward for them, with his butler on the left wing. Only one man, Joe Ditcher, had saved one of Gus's shots by a trick, and he had been signed by Wington City, the Rovers' championship rivals. In a Charities match, Joe Ditcher played against Gus, who missed all his shots, and Ditcher bragged that Gus would not score against him in the Championship decider.

STILL NO SIGN OF GORGEOUS GUS. HIS CAR HASN'T ARRIVED YET—AND EVEN HIS BUTLER DOESN'T KNOW WHAT'S HAPPENED TO HIM.

DON'T WORRY, BOSS. THE MASTER WON'T LET YOU DOWN.

COME ON, LADS.

OKAY, OUT YOU GO! BUT I WISH I HAD YOUR FAITH, BULL. I WISH I KNEW WHERE GORGEOUS GUS WAS.

HEY, THERE'S ONLY NINE OF THEM. WHERE'S GORGEOUS GUS?

HE'LL BE OUT IN A MINUTE. HE AND HIS BUTLER COME FROM THAT FANCY CARAVAN.

I'M SORRY, THE MASTER HAS NOT YET APPEARED. WE WILL START WITH TEN MEN.

THAT'S ALL RIGHT BY ME.

HEY, WHAT'S WRONG WITH GORGEOUS GUS?

I'LL TELL YOU WHAT'S WRONG. HE'S WINDY, THAT'S WHAT. HE'S FRIGHTENED THAT JOE DITCHER WILL MAKE A FOOL OF HIM.

AND NO WONDER HE'S WINDY. LOOK AT THAT SAVE! WHAT A GOALIE!

WHERE'S YOUR MASTER? SULKING IN THAT FANCY CARAVAN OF HIS, I'LL BET. HE'S FRIGHTENED TO FACE ME. I'M THE ONE GOALIE HE CAN'T BEAT.

SHUT YOUR MOUTH ABOUT GORGEOUS GUS, OR YOU'LL GET MY FIST IN IT. I'LL—

STEADY, BULL. I THINK WE CAN SAFELY LEAVE HIM TO THE MASTER.

AND THAT'S HOW I'LL DEAL WITH THE MASTER'S SHOTS, TOO—IF HE EVER COMES OUT TO FACE ME.

As the Rovers had only ten men, Wington soon took the lead. They increased their lead just before half time.

Meanwhile.

NO, I CAN'T PUT THIS RIGHT, I HAVEN'T THE NECESSARY TOOLS.

Two horse-power transport for the stranded centre-forward.

Gus set off with the two horses and steadily made his way nearer Wington and the vital championship decider.

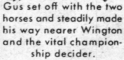

A few minutes later the crowd had something to shout about.

Gorgeous Gus's war of nerves.

The game had to be held up while the groundsmen repaired the post. But soon after the restart, Gus had the ball again.

No refuge for the broken goalie!

STICK IT JOE, LAD. WE'RE STILL ONE UP, AND WE ONLY NEED A DRAW TO WIN THE CHAMPIONSHIP. THERE'S ONLY A FEW MINUTES TO KEEP GUS OUT.

THAT'S ALL RIGHT FOR YOU, CHUM. YOU'RE NOT THE TARGET.

OH, NO! HE'S GOT THE BALL AGAIN.

WHAT ABOUT YOUR JINX, JOE? THOUGHT GORGEOUS GUS COULDN'T SCORE AGAINST YOU?

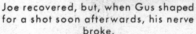

Joe recovered, but, when Gus shaped for a shot soon afterwards, his nerve broke.

LET ME OUT OF HERE!

I CAN'T SHOOT INTO AN EMPTY GOAL. THERE IS NO MERIT IN IT. RAWLINGS, BRING THAT MAN DITCHER TO ME.

SURE, YOUR LORDSHIP.

MY STARS! ONLY ONE GOAL NEEDED TO WIN THE CHAMPIONSHIP, AND HE REFUSES TO SCORE BECAUSE THERE IS NO MERIT IN IT!

I THINK YOU'VE LEARNED YOUR LESSON, DITCHER, SO I'LL LET YOU GO —ON ONE CONDITION. YOU OBTAINED £1000 FROM ME BY FRAUD. PAY THAT MONEY TO THE PLAYERS' BENEVOLENT FUND AND ALL WILL BE WELL.

ANYTHING, YOUR LORDSHIP, I'LL DO ANYTHING RATHER THAN FACE ANY MORE OF YOUR SHOTS.

YAH, WINDY!

HE'S HAD A HARD LESSON, BUT HE ONLY GOT WHAT HE DESERVED.

A minute from the end, with the scores still level, the Rovers got a free kick.

PACK THE GOAL, LADS. HE CAN'T SCORE IF WE PACK THE GOAL—AND A DRAW IS ENOUGH TO GIVE US THE CHAMPIONSHIP.

THAT'S IT, JENKINS. THAT'S JUST WHERE I WANT IT.

PACK THE GOAL, HE SEZ. HE'LL NEVER SCORE IF WE PACK THE GOAL, HE SEZ. HADN'T HE HEARD ABOUT GORGEOUS GUS?

MAKE WAY FOR THE CHAMPIONS!

NO NEED FOR ALL THAT FUSS, MY MEN.

THREE CHEERS FOR GOOD OLD GORGEOUS GUS!

Morgyn the Mighty is fooled — by a cape and some bits of wood!

SEVEN TRAILS TO MORGYN THE MIGHTY

"We must kill him!"

LOOK, THE DEMON WHITE MAN!

QUICKLY, FOLLOW HIM! WE MUST KILL HIM!

MY PLAN IS WORKING!

And so the chase carried on all day with the natives and Packard pursuing Morgyn unsuccessfully. When it grew dark they began to feel afraid . . .

BWANA, I FEEL WE SHOULD RETURN TO CAMP. WE HAVE NOT SEEN THE WHITE FIEND FOR A LONG TIME.

YES, BWANA. THE WHITE ONE WILL BE ABLE TO STRIKE AS HE WISHES IN THE DARKNESS.

YOU WILL DO AS I SAY. THE WHITE MAN WILL APPEAR AGAIN. HE MUST BE IN THIS AREA.

YOU'RE RIGHT PACKARD! I'M UP HERE. CATCH ME IF YOU CAN.

AIEE! THE WHITE FIEND.

GET AFTER HIM!

AFTER HIM. HE MUST NOT ESCAPE!

AIEE, SWAMP! THE DEMON WHITE MAN HAS LED US INTO A SWAMP.

TAKE TO THE TREES. WE'LL BE SAFE THERE.

But the trees weren't as safe as Packard thought . . .

NOW I HAVE HIM!

AAGH!

Packard's struggles grew weaker and weaker until finally —

HE'S DEAD! NOW TO HAVE A WORD WITH THE NATIVE BEARERS.

NOW, YOU MUST LEAVE THE VALLEY. ALL YOUR BWANAS ARE DEAD.

AIEE. HE IS RIGHT. LET US GO.

And so peace reigned once more in the Ompopo valley.

The End

" He's running like a tired cart-horse!"

"I'll track them down!"

A Merry Christmas To All Our Readers *The Editor*

THE VICTOR

EVERY MONDAY

Price 5d

No. 201
DEC. 26th
1964

THE BOXING DAY BATTLE

On December 26th, 1917, German forces attacked the Allied-held positions around Courieres Wood, north of Verdun, in Flanders. They were met by heavy British machine-gun fire.

The Germans laid their plans on Christmas Day.

OUR ARTILLERY WILL OPEN FIRE AT DAWN TOMORROW AND THE INFANTRY WILL GO IN WHEN THE BARRAGE STOPS. THE BRITISH WON'T BE EXPECTING US SO SOON AFTER CHRISTMAS.

At dawn on Boxing Day.

COR, THAT'S A NICE CHRISTMAS PRESENT JERRY'S GIVING US.

GET TO YOUR POSITIONS, LADS. THE ARTILLERY HAS STOPPED AND THE JERRY INFANTRY WILL BE OVER ANY MINUTE NOW.

CONTINUED ON BACK PAGE

The Allied machine-gunners quickly took care of the Germans who had escaped the artillery barrage.

The German attack was repulsed and they did not try again. Their hopes of catching the Allies unprepared on Boxing Day had been shattered.

THE END

PRINTED AND PUBLISHED IN GREAT BRITAIN BY D. C. THOMSON & CO., LTD., AND JOHN LENG & CO., LTD., 12 FETTER LANE, FLEET STREET, LONDON, E.C.4.   © D. C. THOMSON & CO., LTD., 1964.